Charles Dickens & Show Biz

AN EXHIBITION AT THE STANFORD UNIVERSITY LIBRARIES

Charles Dickens & Show Biz

✤ AN EXHIBITION AT
THE STANFORD UNIVERSITY LIBRARIES

✤ CURATED BY RALPH J. CRAWFORD, JR.
& BRUCE J. CRAWFORD

✤ THE STANFORD UNIVERSITY LIBRARIES

STANFORD, CALIFORNIA

2006

Catalogue of an exhibition held at the Stanford University Libraries
2 OCTOBER 2006 – 28 JANUARY 2007

ISBN: 0-911221-37-9

To all those cast in Dickensian roles,
beneath the garish lights.

❦ Contents

✂ Preface

Bruce J. Crawford and Ralph J. Crawford, Jr. proposed *Charles Dickens and Show Biz* to the Stanford University Libraries in the spring of 2005. The exhibition proposal itself was clear evidence of book collectors with a fine sense of purpose and an intellectual curiosity that shaped and defined a spectacular collection. Their suggestion of a Charles Dickens exhibit was of immediate interest to the Stanford Libraries. Dickens's work has near-universal appeal, and we felt that it would be a unique opportunity to host a privately held and developed collection that would complement the Libraries' own holdings of Dickens titles, and be of special interest to the Stanford community. We knew immediately that this exhibit would be both visually and intellectually interesting to Stanford students and faculty, and, just as important, to the larger community.

Charles Dickens and Show Biz brings together materials that show a dimension of Dickens's creative work—his passion for public performance and all aspects of theater—that is not as well known as his fiction. The exhibition tells a compelling story in a new and visually captivating way. Dickens is familiar to many, but his deep association with the theater is not. The exhibit and catalogue have been developed and designed to bring alive the richness and variety of public entertainment that originates from Dickens's work.

It has been a true pleasure for me and my colleague, exhibition designer Becky Fischbach, to work with Bruce J. Crawford and Ralph J. Crawford, Jr. as they've curated this major show featuring their collections. The Crawfords have ever so graciously and generously written and funded the exhibition catalogue to benefit the Stanford University Libraries. Their contributions of time, enthusiasm, and financial support are a wonderful way to share the joys of book collecting and we thank them. The exhibition will surely add to the already broad appeal of the work of Charles Dickens.

ROBERTO G. TRUJILLO
Frances & Charles Field Curator
of Special Collections
Stanford University Libraries

✎ Introduction

Dickens: More Than a Novelist

To mention the name "Charles Dickens" is to call up unforgettable images. The author of *Great Expectations* and *David Copperfield* is remembered for countless characters, such as Scrooge the miser; Tiny Tim, the poor child whom he befriends in *A Christmas Carol*; and Oliver Twist, the parish boy who dares to ask for more. Literary historians tell the rags-to-riches story of the young Dickens who filled bottles in a blacking (shoe polish) warehouse, before he wrote *Pickwick Papers*, which made him famous almost overnight.

However, the second side to Dickens, his passion for public performance and all aspects of the theater, is neglected. This passion drove Dickens to write, produce, direct, and act in theatricals; to include his children and their friends in home-theater performances; and to mount benefit performances in support of worthy causes and indigent friends. For years there was little comment about the strain on Dickens's health resulting from public reading tours of England and America, or about his 1857 performance in *The Frozen Deep*, which led to his liaison with the young actress Ellen Ternan, and the subsequent breakup of his marriage. By comparison to his fame as a novelist, Dickens's prominent connections with the theater remain largely unexplored in contemporary American discussions.

Dickens's love of theatricals was paralleled by efforts of his contemporaries to use his work as source material for the stage. The show biz industry in England and America eagerly piggybacked on Dickens's popularity, releasing hundreds of dramatizations, spoofs, and musical numbers advertised in books, periodicals, and playbills. Prominent actors and actresses specialized in performing as Dickens characters. Well-known stage directors and producers used Dickens's popularity to boost sales of their productions. Adaptations were presented in large halls and neighborhood theaters across Britain and America. Dickens supported some of these efforts, and objected vehemently to others.

Following Dickens's death in 1870, an upturn in stage adaptations, driven by nostalgia and the desire to exploit his work, continued until about 1900. Theatrical activity then slowed, but rebounded after the invention of the silent film, which was followed by hundreds of twentieth-century Dickens entertainments in talking pictures, television and musicals.

About the Stanford Exhibition

Ideally, an exhibition should tell compelling stories in new and visually captivating ways, and should appeal to broad, diverse audiences. *Charles Dickens and Show Biz* is presented with these objectives in mind. While Dickens the novelist is familiar to many, his deep association with theatricals is not. Telling the story of his personal involvement with the stage is the first objective of the exhibition.

The second is to bring alive the richness and variety of public entertainment that derives from his work. Plays and musical adaptations written for the stage have been an important part of the Dickens entertainment canon from 1836 until today. But as public tastes have changed (influenced in part by technological advances in media), once-popular entertainment forms such as tableaux vivants and toy theaters have disappeared, and new forms have taken their place. *Charles Dickens and Show Biz* brings alive these dramatic developments in the entertainment industry.

Some Dickens works, notably *A Christmas Carol* and *Oliver Twist*, have been re-interpreted many times and in many venues. These works endure. This exhibition suggests that the wide appeal of specific themes and subject matter selected by Dickens (e.g. the hope of redemption and spiritual rebirth, and the suffering of neglected children) accounts for this lasting quality of Dickens on the stage and screen.

Advertising has always been an important component of the success or failure of public performances. Through *Charles Dickens and Show Biz*, the visitor can see the evolution of event publicity from its principal form in the 1830s, the theater playbill, through the development of its modern counterparts: movie posters and movie stills, postcards, pressbooks, and advertisements for screenplays, musicals and television productions. Advertising by its nature is designed to capture attention, create awareness, and generate interest in a performance. Likewise, publicity pieces spanning 175 years of theater and entertainment history have their own drama and excitement.

Organization of the Exhibition Catalogue

These exhibition materials are grouped under four main headings. The first section presents items associated with major Dickens novels. The second has items related to Dickens's Christmas books, and the third contains material related to dramatic works written or co-authored by Dickens. The fourth section presents material covering other types of performances, such as tableaux vivants, public readings, and phonograph recordings. Within each category, materials are organized by title or topic: for example, all *Oliver Twist* items are together. Within each title or topic, items are arranged in roughly chronological order.

✍ Curators' Comments

Inter-generational book and ephemera collecting is a rare phenomenon these days. As members of a collecting family that also enjoys music, theater, and film, the Crawfords have been able to support and learn from one another as they have scouted books, formed personal libraries, assembled literary ephemera, and attended stage and screen dramatizations. While the Crawfords enjoy "show biz" from vaudeville to Shakespeare, and from Country and Western to symphonic music, several performances in particular shaped their interest in the theater.

Ralph Crawford Sr. began collecting first editions by Jack London, and was a friend of Russ Kingman (an authority on Jack London). Ralph Sr. also collected Western Americana, especially items related to the California Gold Rush, early San Francisco, and the histories of Western railroading and the Donner party. He remembered one dramatic performance above all others: Lillian Russell's appearance at a Cedar Rapids, Iowa theater in 1905. Known as "The American Beauty" and for forty years the companion of "Diamond Jim" Brady, Iowa-born Russell became one of the foremost actresses and singers of the late nineteenth and early twentieth centuries. She had an hourglass figure and sang racy songs, such as "Oh Those Hips, Oh Those Lips" and "Life Upon the Wicked Stage." Ralph Sr. at age fourteen or fifteen did odd jobs for the theater in Cedar Rapids. Lillian Russell played a one-night stand there, and before her performance asked Ralph Sr. to go out and bring her something to eat. On his return, they sat and talked for half an hour in Lillian's dressing room while waiting for her entrance. In later years, Ralph Sr. often reminisced about Lillian, and knew by heart many songs popular from the 1890s through the 1920s. Ralph Sr.'s wife Dorothy played ragtime piano, and loved to sing and play gay-nineties and Dixieland music.

Ralph Sr.'s son, Ralph Crawford Jr., bought his first rare book in 1953. It was a first edition, in original parts, of Charles Dickens's *The Mystery of Edwin Drood*. In the next decade, he expanded his collecting interests to include the writings of Anthony Trollope and Sir Walter Scott, and then of many British and American poets, from Matthew Prior to Robert Frost. He continues to collect Dickens in depth, concentrating on theatrical and musical adaptations. Ralph Jr. remembers attending with his mother Dorothy a matinee performance of Charlie Chaplin's silent film *The Gold Rush*, at the Chimes Theater in Oakland, California in 1925 or 1926. A typical matinee at the Chimes during the 1920s included a feature film, a Krazy Kat cartoon, a sing-along (in which the audience followed the words and meter by watching a bouncing ball on the screen), and often a three-act vaudeville performance with local, unpaid talent.

Ralph Jr., his wife Helene, and their son Bruce remember the first time they saw a live ballet performance. It was Adolphe Adam's *Giselle*, performed at the Bolshoi Theater in Moscow in 1970. The Crawfords often attended musicals and operas in San Francisco, New York, and London, but when Ralph Jr. and Helene saw Giuseppe Verdi's *Macbeth* at Milan's La Scala Opera House in 1977, it was the most memorable stage event they had ever enjoyed together.

Bruce Crawford was nine when he bought his first rare book in 1963. It was a first edition of *Lives of the Hunted* by Ernest Seton-Thompson, the artist-naturalist. Bruce's other early collecting interests included John Buchan, Jack London, and Lafcadio Hearn. He now collects a range of British and American authors, from John Milton, and early seventeenth-century playwrights, to Thomas Chatterton, George Gissing, and Walter Besant. Bruce's primary collecting interest continues to be William Makepeace Thackeray.

In the midst of enjoying literature and theater in each other's company for many years, Ralph Jr., Helene, and Bruce remember one performance above the rest, as it profoundly changed the direction of their collecting interests and inspired them to gather the material from which the items in this exhibition are drawn. It was a 1962 performance of Lionel Bart's musical *Oliver!* at the Curran Theater in San Francisco. Clive Revill was cast as Fagin, and Georgia Brown as Nancy. Brown's rendition of the song "As Long As He Needs Me" was unforgettable, and inspired the Crawfords to assemble a collection of over one thousand items related to Charles Dickens and the theater.

Bruce's wife Mary collects first editions, continuations, dramatizations, and critical studies of Jane Austen, Mary Webb, and Dorothy L. Sayers. Their son Evan has a collection of angling books. Mary and Bruce have enjoyed numerous recent films based on Austen's best-known novels, *Sense and Sensibility* and *Pride and Prejudice*. In 2004, Mary and Bruce attended a performance of Mary Webb's *Gone to Earth* at the Lyric Theater, Hammersmith. A poster for this performance hangs in the Crawford home, adjacent to those advertising Wilkie Collins's *The Woman in White*, Jack London's *The Sea Wolf*, and William Thackeray's *Vanity Fair*, starring Reese Witherspoon.

A brief look at H. Philip Bolton's landmark book, *Dickens Dramatized*, reveals that the items in this Stanford exhibition illustrate only a very small fraction of the dramatizations produced since 1836. Bolton catalogues three thousand performances, and states that his list is far from complete. This exhibition presents some theatrical high points, but it also includes individual items that are rare, or have unusual interest, or are simply visually exciting and entertaining. After all, one purpose of this exhibition is to entertain, and to entertain is a principal purpose of "show biz."

Acknowledgments

The following books contain much useful information about Charles Dickens and the performing arts: H. Philip Bolton, *Dickens Dramatized* (Boston: G. K. Hall & Co., 1987); F. Dubrez Fawcett, *Dickens the Dramatist on Stage, Screen and Radio* (London: W. H. Allen, 1952); John Forster, *The Life of Charles Dickens*, National Library Edition (New York: Bigelow, Brown and Co., Inc., no date; first published 1872–74); Edgar Johnson, *Charles Dickens, His Tragedy and Triumph* (New York: Simon and Schuster, 1952); Ephraim Katz, *The Film Encyclopedia*, 4th edition, revised by Fred Klein and Ronald Dean Nolen (New York: Harper Resource, an imprint of HarperCollins Publishers, 2001).

The Internet Movie Database (at www.imdb.com) provides useful information about motion pictures, actors, and actresses.

We are grateful for the kind assistance and support of the following individuals: Mr. Roberto Trujillo and Ms. Becky Fischbach, Department of Special Collections, Stanford University; Ms. Sally Treadway, The Associates of the Stanford University Libraries; Mr. Charles Berliner, Theatrical Scenery and Costume Designer.

We thank the following organizations for access to archive material, and for permissions to exhibit and publish: The California Historical Society, FN-16862, FN-19627; The Cleveland Playhouse; The Dickens House Museum, London; The Manchester City Council, Department of Libraries and Theaters; The Manchester Library and Information Service: Manchester Arts Library.

We are especially grateful to Mr. Jerry Kelly, who designed our book, and to Mr. Frank Sypher, our excellent editor. As always, Mary and Helene Crawford, in lending their advice, encouragement and support, were loving and steadfast.

Exhibition Catalogue

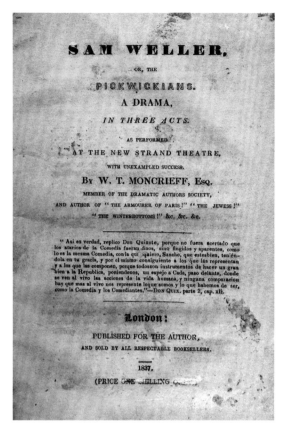

NO. 1

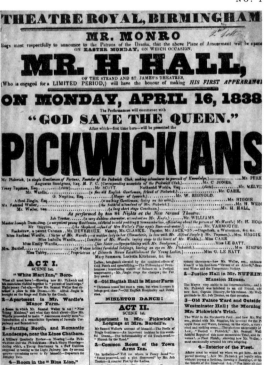

NO. 2

NO. 3

❧ Pickwick Papers

The full title of Charles Dickens's Pickwick Papers—The Posthumous Papers of the Pickwick Club —hints at comic adventures to come. Page one records the minutes of a Pickwick Club meeting:

"May 12, 1817. Joseph Smiggers, Esq., P.V.P.M.P.C.* presiding. The following resolutions unanimously agreed to.

"That this Association has heard read, with feelings of unmingled satisfaction, and unqualified approval, the paper communicated by Samuel Pickwick, Esq., G.C.M.P.C.† entitled "Speculations on the Source of the Hampstead Ponds, with some Observations on the Theory of Tittlebats;" and that this Association does hereby return its warmest thanks to the said Samuel Pickwick, Esq., G.C.M.P.C. for the same."

** Perpetual Vice-President—Member Pickwick Club.—*ED.
*† General Chairman—Member Pickwick Club.—*ED.

Pickwick Papers *chronicles the misadventures of the four Pickwickians: Samuel Pickwick, Tracy Tupman, Augustus Snodgrass, and Nathaniel Winkle. They are joined by Sam Weller, manservant to Mr. Pickwick, who becomes a principal character. The five travelers experience one catastrophe after another, from an encounter with a drunken cabman, to Mrs. Bardell's suit against Mr. Pickwick for breach of promise. The reader knows that despite all of these difficulties, "everything will turn out all right in 'the Pickwickian sense.'" The comic episodes encountered by Sam Weller and the Pickwickians have made readers and audiences laugh since 1836.*

1. W. T. Moncrieff. *Sam Weller. Or, the Pickwickians. A Drama in Three Acts.* London: Published for the Author, 1837.

   WITH: Reproduction of the front cover of *Actors by Daylight*, May 12, 1838.

   Charles Dickens's first major book, *Pickwick Papers*, was issued in monthly parts beginning in 1836. While the parts were still coming out, an enterprising playwright, W. T. Moncrieff, published this play as performed at the New Strand Theatre. The play was first performed on April 3, and ran until October 12, 1837. Dickens protested against this piracy of his book, and Moncrieff defended his plagiarism in an advertisement which was published together with the text of the play. The most famous actor in *Sam Weller* was W. J. Hammond, who is portrayed in the title role on the front cover of the May 12, 1838 issue of *Actors by Daylight*.

2. [Playbill] Theatre Royal, Birmingham. April 16, 1838. Announcing a performance of *Pickwickians*.

   The featured actor was Mr. H. Hall in the role of Sam Weller's father, Tony Weller. In 1837 Hall had played the part of Tony Weller in *Sam Weller, or the Pickwickians*. Mr. H. Webb, who was apparently a regular performer at the Theatre Royal, Birmingham, had the leading roles in two afterpieces on this playbill, *The Christening*, and *Black Anna's Bower!*

3. [Playbill] Theatre Royal, Drury Lane [London]. December 6, 1869. Announcing a performance of *Bardell v. Pickwick*.

   This playbill, announcing a "Grand Benefit in Aid of the Charles Harcourt Memorial Fund," is of special interest. Charles Dickens is listed as a member of the Executive

Committee of the Memorial Fund. The program concludes with the trial scene *Bardell v. Pickwick* from *Pickwick Papers*, arranged from Charles Dickens's reading edition by John Hollingshead and Dickens (a reading edition is a condensation made by Dickens for use as text at his readings). Hollingshead had a long association with Dickens, having been on the staff of *Household Words*, the magazine published by Dickens. This performance of *Bardell v. Pickwick* ran only once, on Monday morning, December 6, 1869, at the Theatre Royal, Drury Lane. Dickens was in the cast as a member of the jury. Other notable members of the cast were Ellen Farren as Sam Weller, and Horace Wigan as Mr. Phunkey.

4. [Sheet Music] Charles Hausman. *The Pickwickians, A Sett of Quadrilles.* Philadelphia: John F. Nunns, 1838.

The music consists of four quadrilles dedicated to the four members of the Pickwick Club: Samuel Pickwick, Tracy Tupman, Nathaniel Winkle, and Augustus Snodgrass. The set concludes with "The Pickwickian Waltz."

5. [Sheet Music] J. W. Turner. *Pickwick Galop.* Boston: Oliver Ditson & Co., 1867.

Interestingly, the cover depicts a careworn Dickens, who in 1867 was fifty-five years old.

6. [Sheet Music] Grant Stewart and Manuel Klein. *Boys Will Be Boys.* New York: M. Witmark & Sons, 1902.

During Charles Dickens's lifetime, dramatizations of his stories flourished. Hundreds of adaptations were produced. Upon his death in 1870, there was a surge in popularity of such plays, with almost five hundred being staged between 1870 and 1890. Then, between

NO. 4

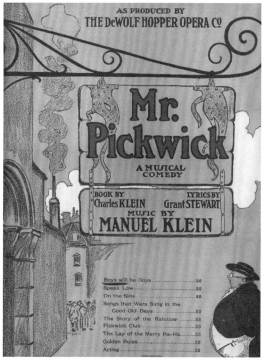

NO. 6

the last decade of the nineteenth century and the introduction of silent films in the early 1900s, the number of productions declined.

This song is from *Mr. Pickwick, A Musical Comedy in Two Acts*. It was produced by the DeWolf Hopper Opera Co. in 1903. The play was written by Charles Klein. It opened in New York on January 19, 1903 at the Herald Square Theater, and ran for thirty-two performances. DeWolf Hopper had the starring role, as Mr. Pickwick. The play was subsequently performed in Newark and Denver.

7. [Sheet Music] Claude Debussy. *Hommage à S. Pickwick Esq. P.P.M.P.C.* [Posthumous Papers of the Members of the Pickwick Club]. Paris: Durand & Cie, 1913.

8. [Movie Poster] *Pickwicker*. Vitagraph, 1913.

NO. 7

John Bunny was in the leading role as Samuel Pickwick. Bunny grew up in Brooklyn. He ran away to join a roving minstrel show, and then progressed in show business as an actor, stage manager, and director. In 1910, Bunny became associated with Vitagraph, where he quickly became the first comic star of American silent films. On upper Broadway stand the remains of the Bunny Theater, built by Bunny (two masonry rabbit heads adorn the façade).

Bunny weighed over three hundred pounds and in addition to playing a comic Mr. Pickwick, he made more than 150 short comedies. He also played a dramatic role in *Vanity Fair*.

9. Cosmo Hamilton and Frank C. Reilly. *"Pickwick" A Play in Three Acts*. New York: G. P. Putnam's Sons, 1927.

This play was probably the most successful of the twentieth-century adaptations of *Pickwick*. It was first performed in Washington, D.C., on February 15, 1927. Samuel Pickwick was played by John Cumberland; and Sam Weller by Charles McNaughton. The play had a successful run in Washington, D.C., and then played in New York City at the Empire Theater for seventy-two performances. It was then performed at the Haymarket Theatre, London, with Charles Laughton as Mr. Pickwick.

10. [Sheet Music] Cyril Ornadel and Leslie Bricusse. *If I Ruled the World*. London and New York: Delfont Music, Ltd. and Chappell & Co., Ltd., 1963.

"If I Ruled the World" is from the David Merrick/Bernard Delfont musical comedy *Pickwick*. Wolf Mankowitz wrote the play. *Pickwick* was performed many times in Britain and America during the 1960s and 70s.

11. Charles Dickens. *Our Mutual Friend.* London: Chapman & Hall, Ltd., no date.

WITH: a newspaper clipping from the *San Francisco Chronicle*, undated [1974].

The newspaper clipping is of a photograph of Rebecca Ann King, Miss America 1974. In the pageant's talent competition, she sang "If I Ruled the World," from the musical *Pickwick*. The reading copy of *Our Mutual Friend* is inscribed: "My best to Ralph Crawford in admiration of our mutual friend Charles Dickens. Rebecca King Miss America 1974."

✎ Oliver Twist

O liver Twist *has lasting appeal for audiences of all ages. The poor orphan Oliver, who has the courage to challenge brutal authority by asking "Please, sir, I want some more," and the book's grim ending, both pull at the heartstrings of readers, playgoers, and cinephiles. Adults are moved by the action that portrays brutal conditions in nineteenth-century England: the plight of uncared-for infants in "baby farms" and the sale of those orphans who survive; the manipulation of pickpocket gangs by the villainous Fagin; the pistol-whipping murder of Nancy by Bill Sikes, and Fagin's execution by hanging before a pushy crowd of smoking, card-playing, joking onlookers.*

12. George Almar. *Oliver Twist.* London: John Dicks Press, Ltd., no date. Dicks' Standard Plays No. 293.

A dramatization by George Almar of *Oliver Twist*, staged at the Royal Surrey Theatre on November 19, 1838, and reprinted by John Dicks Press. The full title was: *Oliver Twist, A Serio Comic Burletta, In Three Acts.* Dickens attended a performance, and was so distressed that he lay down in dismay on the floor of his box. Nevertheless, the play had a highly successful run of eighty-six performances at the Surrey, and was revived several times. The cast included Master Owen as Oliver, W. Smith as Bumble, and E. F. Saville as Sikes.

13. [Anonymous] *Oliver Twist or the Parish Boy's Progress.* No place, no date [England, circa late 1800s].

Charles Dickens was a sickly child, and while other boys played cricket and other active

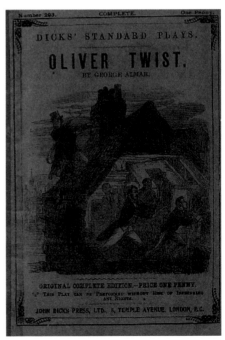

OLIVER TWIST.

ACT I.

SCENE 1. No. 1. THE INTERIOR OF THE "THREE CRIPPLES." Wings No. 1.

The Tables with THIEVES—and BATES & DODGER Playing at Cards, in Set Piece, to be put on.

Enter FAGIN, Right Hand & BILL SIKES, Left Hand—Pl. 2.

Fagin. 'Tis gold! By my soul, a bargain!
Sikes. What are you jawing about, Fagin?
Dodger. Fagin's got a bargain, that's all.
Sikes. Who has he been swindling, the old thief?
Fagin. No one. A pauper met me in the street, just now, and sold me this watch.
Sikes. And how should a pauper have a watch?
Fagin. It was given her by a woman she attended, fourteen years ago. I'll tell you all about it.

Enter MONKS, Left Hand—Plate 3. *(he retires back.)*

Fagin. About fourteen years ago, said the pauper, they discovered her in the road, worn out with fatigue and want, Within three hours of her being brought to the workhouse, she gave birth to a male child and expired. As a reward for her services, she gave the woman who attended her this watch.
Sikes. But what became of the child?
Fagin. At the workhouse. They call him Oliver Twist.
Monks. *(coming forward)* Fagin, I am glad to see you, I overheard your tale—that trinket—let me see it.
Fagin. Yes, yes, Mr. Monks, in a moment—there is a cypher on it—"H. B. The gift of a fond father."
Monks. Those initials too!—That cypher! By Heaven, I was not deceived!—'twas hers—'twas hers!
Fagin. You knew the owner of this watch, then?
Monks. Knew her? Would I ne'er had seen her—I had then been a crimeless man. Ask me nothing—thoughts of the past torture me. Must I be ever haunted thus!
Fagin. An advertisement by the Board of St. Nicholas' Workhouse, offering a premium of five pounds to any tradesman who will take Oliver Twist as an apprentice.
Monks. Fagin that boy's fate is involved with mine, Get him and you shall have a hundred pounds.
Fagin. And what would you do with him, Mr. Monks?
Monks. No harm—but we must have him in our power.
Fagin. You want to have this boy in your power? Vell, it shall be done. Dawkins! Bates!

games, Charles read books. When Charles was six or seven he wrote a play, *Misnar, the Sultan of India*, which he performed with childhood friends. The manuscript for *Misnar* has not survived.

When Charles was nine or ten his cousin James Lamert made a toy theater for him, which enabled Charles to visualize and perform plays based on his reading of works such as *Roderick Random*, *Tom Jones*, and *The Arabian Nights*.

Toy theaters were popular children's playthings during the mid-nineteenth century. They were distributed by a number of publishers, including Skelt, J. K. Green, and Pollack. The toy included an abbreviated story, with dramatic parts suitable for young readers. Sketches of the characters and sets were printed on heavy paper stock, and these could be cut out and positioned inside a tabletop stage. Children then reassembled the cutouts to create the various scenes in the play. Uncolored cutouts sold for a penny; colored, for two pence.

This item, privately published by an unidentified Dickens enthusiast (one of only twelve copies), includes both a toy theater script, and the cutouts for *Oliver Twist* as distributed by Green in 1846. *Oliver Twist* was the only novel by Dickens to be adapted for toy theaters.

14. Robert Louis Stevenson. *Memories & Portraits*. London: Chatto and Windus, 1887.

This work contains Stevenson's essay "A Penny Plain and Twopence Coloured," which inspired a revival of interest in toy theaters. Stevenson writes of his own collection of toy theaters (which did not include Green's *Oliver Twist*).

15. [Playbill] National Theater, Boston. January 23, 1852. Announcing a performance of *Oliver Twist or The Workhouse Boy's Progress*.

Oliver Twist was Dickens's second major book. As with *Pickwick*, stage versions appeared before the novel had finished its serial run (in *Bentley's Miscellany*). By the 1850s, *Oliver Twist* had played in more than forty theaters in Great Britain and America. This performance was a benefit for Fanny Wallack; in previous performances in America she had made her own the role of Nancy. The playbill also announces that Fanny Wallack would appear in *Clari, the Maid of Milan* and would sing "Home Sweet Home." It is interesting to note that in the early 1830s Charles Dickens, while still a shorthand reporter, participated in an amateur theatrical production of *Clari, the Maid of Milan*. The authorship of *Clari* (first produced in 1823) is credited either to J. R. Planché, or to John Howard Payne, but the play was later performed in many adaptations and reworkings.

While Dickens did not act in the 1852 version of *Clari*, he was producer, director, and stage manager. Thus, *Clari* is a forerunner of many later theatricals which Dickens produced and directed, and in which he also acted.

NO. 15   NO. 16

16. [Playbill] Theatre Halifax, Yorkshire. March 14, 1856. Announcing a performance of *Oliver Twist! Or, the Parish Boy's Progress!*

The performance was for the benefit of Mr. R. Ross, who played the part of the Artful Dodger. Neither the playbill nor any of the cast are recorded in H. Philip Bolton's *Dickens Dramatized*. The playbill illustrates the popularity of Dickens dramatizations in relatively small towns such as Halifax in Yorkshire, where members of the cast were apparently little-known local actors and actresses. On the evening of March 14, Mr. R. Ross also played Aminidab Sleak in the comedy *The Serious Family* and Jem Boggs in *The Wandering Minstrel*. He also sang "The Statty Fair!" in which he introduced a mock cachuca [*sic*] and sailor's hornpipe. Mr. R. Ross certainly earned whatever money he may have derived from his benefit. The cachucha had been popularized by Fanny Elssler and Pauline Duvernay, two star dancers of the period. The dance had a brief revival of popularity in America in 1990.

17. [Theater Program] His Majesty's Theatre, London [1905].

Announcing the last week of dramatizations of *Oliver Twist* in July 1905. His Majesty's Theatre was owned and managed by Sir Herbert Beerbohm Tree. This play was dramatized by J. Comyns Carr. It starred Herbert Tree as Fagin, and Constance Collier as Nancy.

24]

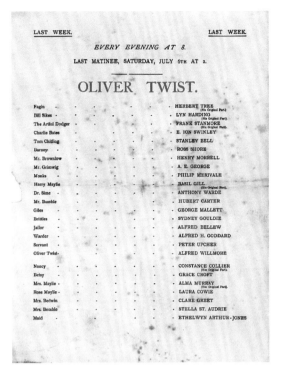

NO. 17   NO. 18

18. [Postcard] *Miss Constance Collier and Mr. Beerbohm Tree in "Oliver Twist."*
[England]: Rotary Photographic [1905].

Sir Herbert Beerbohm Tree appears as
Fagin, and Constance Collier as Nancy.

19. [Playbill] Morosco Theater, Los Angeles.
February 17, 1913.

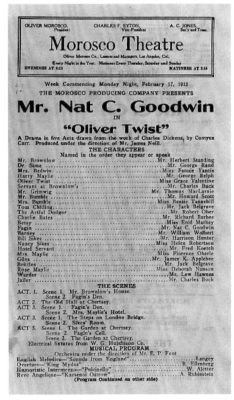

NO. 19

Announcing a performance of *Oliver
Twist*. The performance was a drama in five
acts, drawn from the work of Charles
Dickens by Comyns Carr. It starred Nat C.
Goodwin as Fagin.

20. [Sheet Music] Vaughn De Leath. *Oliver
Twist*. New York: M. Witmark & Sons, 1922.

WITH: a program from the Theatre Royal,
Manchester: January 29, 1923. Announcing
a performance of *Oliver Twist*, with Jackie
Coogan.

The sheet music was published to accompa-
ny the silent film *Oliver Twist*, with Coogan
in the starring role. The theater program,
listing Coogan as the star, also announces

[25

Lon Chaney in the role of Fagin. The front cover of this program reads "Meet Your Friends at the Theatre Royal." The back cover includes the notation: "'What's His is His.' Jackie Coogan has been legally adopted by his own mother. This was done to safeguard the boy's financial interests . . . Mr. and Mrs. Coogan believed the Public was entitled to know that Jackie's earnings would go into Jackie's coffers and into no other's."

Coogan was born in 1914, and his career as a child actor was phenomenal. He was among Hollywood's highest-paid performers. As a child he received $500,000 for switching from the filmmaker First National to Metro. This money and most of his salary were kept in trust by his parents.

In 1928, Coogan headlined a show

at the London Palladium, after having played his last role as a child star the year before. However, by the 1930s Coogan was almost forgotten.

In 1935, when he turned twenty-one, Coogan was to receive the $4 million he had earned as a child actor. However, his father died in an automobile accident, in which Coogan was injured. His mother then remarried, and she and the stepfather were not inclined to part with the money, so the dispute ended up in court. By the time the court proceedings were adjudicated, the funds had dwindled to only $252,000 of which Jackie Coogan received half. The Coogan litigation led to the passage of the Child Actor's Bill, popularly known as the Coogan Act, which was designed to prevent child actors from being swindled by financial trustees.

Coogan married Betty Grable in 1937; they divorced in 1940. He carried on with his career, appearing many times on screen and on TV. He died in 1984. Coogan is perhaps best remembered today for his role as Uncle Fester in the TV series *The Addams Family*.

21. [Newspaper Comics] "Parlor Bedroom & Sink by Billy De Beck." *America's Greatest Color Comic Section, King Features Syndicate, Inc.*, July 24, 1932.

WITH: "Parlor, Bedroom and Sink – Starring Bunky by Billy De Beck." *America's Greatest Color Comic Section, King Features Syndicate, Inc.*, September 10, 1933.

The characters in the first comic strip are Bunky, an orphan waif and Fagan [*sic*]. The artist Billy De Beck portrays Fagan (from *Oliver Twist*, but spelled thus) as an Irishman. In the second comic strip, Fagin (usual spelling) is portrayed as a Jew. Both strips are early appearances in comic form of Dickens characters from *Oliver Twist*.

22. [VCR Tape] *Oliver Twist*. Alpha Video Distributors, Inc., 1996; a re-release of a film originally produced in 1933.

    Dickie Moore starred as Oliver in this 1933 production of *Oliver Twist*. This production was the first sound film of Dickens's novel. Moore was a popular child actor in the 1930s.

23. [Movie Poster] *Oliver Twist*. The J. Arthur Rank Organization and Eagle Lion Classics, 1951.

    This movie version starred Alec Guinness, Robert Newton, Kay Walsh and Francis L. Sullivan.

24. [Photo Stills] Untitled still showing Oliver Twist.

    WITH: "God is Love" from *Oliver Twist*, 1951.

    These two stills show scenes from the J. Arthur Rank production (1951).

25. [Sheet Music] Lionel Bart. *Vocal Selections from "Oliver!"* London and New York: Lakeview Music Co. and Hollis Music, Inc., 1960.

    This musical version starred Clive Revill as Fagin, and Georgia Brown as Nancy. Georgia Brown's rendition of "As Long as He Needs Me" became a classic identified with the musical.

26. [Photo Stills] Untitled still showing Oliver Twist.

    WITH: Untitled still showing Fagin from *Oliver!* (1968).

    These two scenes are from Lionel Bart's *Oliver!* The Romulus production was released by Columbia Pictures in 1968. Ron Moody starred as Fagin, and Shani Wallis as Nancy. When this film won seven academy awards, including best picture, the academy presentation and acceptance speeches thanked everyone from the producer to the wardrobe girl. One name was not mentioned: Charles Dickens. That's Hollywood.

27. [CD Press Kit] *Oliver Twist*. Sony Pictures Entertainment, Inc., 2005.

    Oliver Twist, a Roman Polanski film, starred Ben Kingsley as Fagin. In addition to winning an academy award for directing *The Pianist*, Polanski had Oscar nominations as best director for *Chinatown* in 1974 and for *Tess* in 1979. Kingsley won an academy award for best actor in the title role of *Gandhi* in 1982.

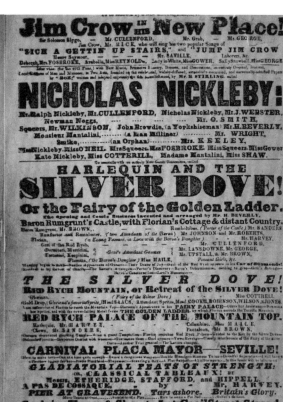

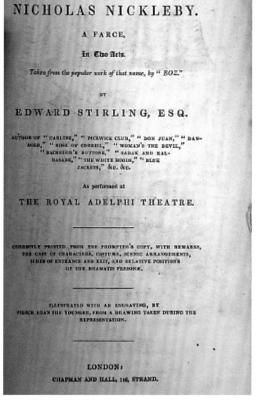

᪣ Nicholas Nickleby

*I*n Nicholas Nickleby *Charles Dickens highlights conditions in Yorkshire schools. Dotheboys Hall is an establishment where unwanted children are sent to be boarded and presumably educated. The schoolmaster is Wackford Squeers, brutal and ignorant, as is revealed when he tries to teach a class how to spell "botany" upon hearing that a student, rather than attending class, has been weeding the garden:*

"B-o-t, bot, t-i-n, tin, bottin, n-e-y, ney, bottinney, noun substantive, a knowledge of plants. When he has learned that bottiney means a knowledge of plants, he goes and knows 'em. That's our system, Nickleby; what do you think of it?" Nicholas responds "It's a very useful one, at any rate."

The abused, disadvantaged, or neglected child is found frequently in Dickens's novels. Poor Smike, another of Squeers's hapless pupils and a principal character in Nicholas Nickleby, *is one. Oliver Twist, Little Nell, Tiny Tim, Paul Dombey, Poor Jo, and Little Dorrit are others. The helpless child theme, sad but popular, has been explored and exploited many times in Dickens dramatizations since* Nicholas Nickleby *appeared in 1839.*

28. [Playbill] Theatre Royal, Adelphi [London]. January 14, 1839. Announcing a performance of *Nicholas Nickleby*.

    This two-act farce, the first dramatization of Dickens's novel, was written by Edward Stirling, who dedicated it to Dickens. It was performed at the Royal Adelphi Theatre, London, and ran from November 19, 1838 to February 11, 1839, a total of 160 performances. This playbill is for the performance on Monday, January 14, 1839. Note the diversity of entertainment offered the audience on the evening of January 14. *Nicholas Nickleby* shared the bill with the *Adelphi Giant! Mons. Bihin, (The Tallest Man in the World!)*. Also on the bill is *Harlequin and the Silver Dove! Or the Fairy of the Golden Ladder.*

29. Edward Stirling. *Nicholas Nickleby. A Farce, in Two Acts*. London: Chapman and Hall [mid-1800s].

    This play was dedicated by Stirling to Dickens. It was first performed at the Royal Adelphi Theatre, London on November 19, 1838. The play was produced after only eight monthly parts of the novel had been published. Mrs. Keeley starred in the role of Smike. H. Philip Bolton, author of *Dickens Dramatized*, writes that Dickens saw the play twice and praised Mrs. Keeley's performance as Smike. However, Dickens also "objected to the adaptation of any unfinished work, badly done and worse acted." Stirling's play had an improbable ending, in which Smike inherits a fortune. Smike's closing speech was: "I hope that we have been fortunate enough to secure the good wishes and approbation of a numerous circle of kind friends, (pointing to the audience,) who by their generous sympathy and support, will ensure the future career of Smike and Nicholas Nickleby."

30. [Sheet Music] Anonymous. *Nicholas Nickleby*. Boston: Oliver Ditson [mid-1800s].

    This piece is noted as being composed and arranged for the pianoforte.

31. [Film Script] *The Life and Adventures of Nicholas Nickleby*. London: Ealing Studios, 1947.

The post-production shooting script with full dialogue, music, sound effects, and action continuity for *The Life and Adventures of Nicholas Nickleby*.

32. [Film Script] Ray Bradbury. *Any Friend of Nicholas Nickleby's is a Friend of Mine. A Play*. No place, no date [circa 1971–72].

Ray Bradbury wrote a short story with this title in 1968, and then wrote this play in 1971–72 but did not produce it. Thirty-five or forty copies of the play were run off by Bradbury for distribution to his friends. In the play, Dickens appears as one of the principal characters, as does the poet Emily Dickinson. Other authors are mentioned, including Jane Austen, Thomas Hardy, and Nathaniel Hawthorne. Frequent references are made in the play to Dickens's *A Tale of Two Cities*, and many of his other works are mentioned. Bradbury is probably best known for his fantasy science fiction, including *The Martian Chronicles* (1950), and for his novel *Fahrenheit 451* (1953).

33. [Television Series Poster] *The Life and Adventures of Nicholas Nickleby*. The Royal Shakespeare Company and the Mobil Showcase Network, 1983.

Peter Ustinov was the host and narrator. This version of *Nicholas Nickleby* was a nine-hour series, broadcast over four consecutive nights.

34. [Photo Still] Untitled still, showing the Nicklebys from *The Life and Adventures of Nicholas Nickleby*, 1983.

A promotional still, showing the principal members of the cast of *Nicholas Nickleby*, produced by the Royal Shakespeare Company. Left to right are: Roger Rees as Nicholas Nickleby; Emily Richards as Nicholas's sister Kate; Jane Downs, their mother; and John Woodvine, their avaricious uncle, Ralph Nickleby.

❦ The Old Curiosity Shop

*I*n The Old Curiosity Shop, *Little Nell and her grandfather, a compulsive gambler, fall into the clutches of the evil Quilp. The death of Little Nell caused readers of the serial, including Sir Francis Jeffrey (editor of the* Edinburgh Review, *Scottish M.P., and influential literary critic), to implore Dickens not to let Little Nell die. Jeffrey and many others, including William Macready, Thomas Carlyle, and Walter Savage Landor, were deeply saddened by Little Nell's death. Dickens's biographer Edgar Johnson says that with this novel, Dickens strengthened the personal bond between himself and his readers, and established his mastery of pathos.*

35. [Playbill] Theatre Royal, Portsmouth. September 14–16, 1871. Announcing a performance of *Little Nelly*.

This "Celebrated Version" of Dickens's *The Old Curiosity Shop* was produced by G. Murray and consisted of four acts. Miss Virginia Blackwood starred in two roles: as Little Nelly and as the Marchioness. Blackwood starred in many plays adapted from Dickens's novels, including *Barnaby Rudge, David Copperfield*, and *Bleak House*. After the initial performances in Portsmouth, *Little Nelly* opened in London at the Surrey on November 23, 1872.

NO. 35   NO. 36

36. George Lander. *The Old Curiosity Shop. A Drama in Four Acts.* London: John Dicks, no date. Dicks' Standard Plays No. 398.

This play was adapted by George Lander from Dickens's novel, and first performed at the Theatre Royal, York on May 14, 1877. The illustration on the cover of the play is of Dick Swiveller and the Marchioness. This copy was apparently used by an actor playing the part of the "Single Gentleman"; the entrances, exits and speaking parts for that role are underlined in red.

37. [Sheet Music] William F. Gilchrest and E. G. Sirret. *The Grave of Little Nell.* No place, no date.

WITH: George Linley. *Little Nell.* New York: C. H. Ditson & Co., no date.

These two pieces of sheet music mourn the death of Little Nell. "The Grave of Little Nell" concludes: "Oft my tears be-dew the roses O'er the grave of little Nell."

   "Little Nell" sung by D. S. Wambold of the San Francisco Minstrels, and dedicated to Charles Dickens, hopefully concludes: "'Hush! Hush!' he said, 'she only sleeps, She'll wake again tomorrow.'"

NO. 37

38. [Song Sheet] Casserly and T. Bissell. *Little Nell.* New York: H. De Marsan, no date [mid-1800s].

This song is similar to "Little Nell" sung by D. S. Wambold of the San Francisco Minstrels. Both quote the dying words of Little Nell's grandfather: "She'll wake again to-morrow."

39. [Pressbook] *The Old Curiosity Shop.* Time-Life Television and BBC-TV, 1979.

This television dramatization of *The Old Curiosity Shop* was released in 1979. Little Nell's grandfather, played by Sebastian Shaw, appears on the pressbook cover. The production was one of the "Once Upon a Classic" series hosted by Bill Bixby.

40. [Photo Still] Untitled still showing Little Nell and Dick Swiveller from *Mister Quilp*, 1975.

In the 1970s, Reader's Digest Films produced a series of family-oriented movies. These included *Tom Sawyer*, *Huckleberry Finn*, and *Mister Quilp*, which was based on Dickens's *The Old Curiosity Shop. Mister Quilp* was released in the United Kingdom on December 26, 1975, opening in London's West End. The film had opened in New York on November 12th. It opened at ten theaters in Los Angeles on the 19th, and in 150 theaters around the United States on November 20, 1975.

    Mister Quilp starred Anthony Newley as the villainous Mr. Quilp, Michael Hordern as Nell's grandfather, David Hemmings as Dick Swiveller, and Sarah Jane Varley as Little Nell.

    The musical adaptation of *Mister Quilp* had a large cast, with Sarah Jane Varley and David Hemmings giving outstanding performances in the musical numbers. Varley was only twelve when she was selected from among five hundred young hopefuls auditioning for the role of Little Nell. David Hemmings entered show business at the age of nine as a boy soprano. He began appearing in British films in the late 1950s, and continued his career as a film director in the 1970s.

41. [Drawing] G. Scott. *The Old Curiosity Shop. Preliminary Scheme for Fairground.* November 1, 1973.

The artist's sketch for a scene in *Mister Quilp*, the musical adapted from *The Old Curiosity Shop*. Note that in 1973 the developing production was still referred to as *The Old Curiosity Shop* rather than as *Mister Quilp*. This item is a preliminary sketch for the "Fairgrounds" scene.

42. [Film Script] *Mister Quilp.* London: Reader's Digest Films, Ltd., 1975.

The complete post-production script for *Mister Quilp*, dated May 1975. This page shows the action and dialogue for a portion of the "Fairgrounds" scene.

✎ Barnaby Rudge

Barnaby Rudge *is a historical novel concerning the Lord Gordon "No Popery" riots of 1780. The story pleads for religious tolerance, and stands as a public statement against public executions and capital punishment for minor crimes (Dickens often and vigorously opposed these punishments). The novel was dramatized frequently in the nineteenth century. Playgoers especially liked Barnaby Rudge, the half-crazed youth who walked about with a raven named Grip perched on his shoulder (Dickens also had a pet raven named Grip); and Dolly Varden, a coquettish young girl, good humored, and beautiful.*

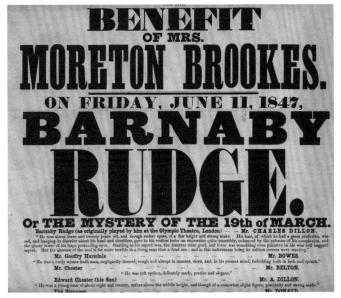

NO. 43   NO. 44

43. [Playbill] Theatre Royal, Wolverhampton. June 11, 1847. Announcing a performance of *Barnaby Rudge*.

Barnaby Rudge, one of Dickens's less familiar novels, was dramatized almost twenty times between the date of its publication in the fall of 1841 and June 11, 1847 (the performance advertised by this playbill). This performance was produced at the Theatre Royal, Wolverhampton by Charles Dillon, who played the role of Barnaby Rudge. Dillon was an accomplished Dickens actor. He had also performed in *Oliver Twist*, *Martin Chuzzlewit*, *The Cricket on the Hearth* and *The Battle of Life*. The performance on June 11, 1847 was for the benefit of Mrs. Moreton Brookes, who was cast as Barnaby's mother.

44. [Sheet Music] E. Mack. *Dolly Varden Quadrille*. Philadelphia: Lee & Walker, 1872.

WITH: Frank W. Green and Alfred Lee. *Dolly Varden*. Cleveland: S. Brainard's Sons, 1872.

Illustrations on these pieces of sheet music show the nineteenth-century women's garment called a "Dolly Varden," named after Dickens's colorfully dressed character. Incidentally, the Dolly Varden trout and the Dolly Varden crab (also known as the calico crab) take their names from Dickens's character. Lyrics in the second piece of sheet music are: "Oh! have you seen my little girl? / She doesn't wear a bonnet. / She's got a monstrous flip-flop hat / With cherry ribbons on it; / She dresses in bed furniture, / Just like a flower garden, / A blowin' and a growin' and / They call it 'Dolly Varden.'"

45. Charles Dickens. *Mrs. Gamp with the Strolling Players*. New York: Privately printed, 1899.

In 1847 Dickens's friend Leigh Hunt was in financial difficulties. Dickens and his group of amateur actors decided to come to Hunt's aid and staged Ben Jonson's *Every Man in His Humour*. It was performed twice in 1847, at Manchester and Liverpool. However, the amount raised for Hunt's benefit (just over four hundred pounds) fell short of Dickens's expectations by about one hundred pounds.

To raise this amount Dickens planned to write a humorous sketch to be written in the character of "Mrs. Gamp," from *Martin Chuzzlewit*. Unfortunately, the enterprise was terminated, and only one chapter of Mrs. Gamp's monologue was written. The little farce was to be entitled *A New Piljian's Projiss*, written by Mrs. Gamp, and edited by Charles Dickens. The book exhibited here, *Mrs. Gamp with the Strolling Players*, was printed for Lowell Palmer, who owned Dickens's manuscript. Only eighty-five copies were published. The sketch lampoons many of the amateur actors in the benefit performances, including Augustus Egg, Mark Lemon, Douglas Jerrold, George Cruikshank, and Dickens himself.

46. [Pressbook] *Martin Chuzzlewit*. Thomas A. Edison Films, 1912.

This early three-reel film starred William West and George Lessey. The illustrated pressbook provides a detailed plot synopsis. The front cover is stamped "Queen's Hall / Electric Theatre / Newington Butts, S E."

47. [Playbill] New York. August 31, 1848. Announcing a performance of *Dombey and Son*. Philip Bolton documents in *Dickens Dramatized* that this performance took place at Burton's Tripler Hall Theater.

This dramatization was by John Brougham, who was also cast in the roles of Major Bagstock and Jack Bunsby. Mrs. Brougham played Susan Nipper, and the famous comedian John Burton was in the cast in his most famous role, Captain Cuttle.

48. [Sheet Music] Mrs. John MacFarren. *Dombey & Son*. New York: Firth, Pond & Co., 1848.

WITH: Charles Jefferys. *Florence, The Study of a Loving Heart*. New York: Firth, Pond & Co., no date.

WITH: Joseph Edwards Carpenter and Stephen Glover. *What Are the Wild Waves Saying*. London: Messrs. Robert Cocks & Co., no date.

These three pieces of sheet music derive from *Dombey and Son*. The first, *Dombey & Son*, by Mrs. MacFarren, has five movements dedicated to five characters: Mr. Dombey ("The First Consideration"); Florence ("The Study of a loving heart"); Carker ("The Trusty Agent"); Edith ("The Haughty Beauty"); and Captain Cuttle ("When found make a Note on"). The second piece, *Florence, The Study of a Loving Heart*, has a quotation from page 472 of the first edition of *Dombey and Son*. Florence Dombey, having been struck by her father, "saw that she had no father upon earth, and ran out, orphaned, from his house." The third piece, *What Are the Wild Waves Saying,* is a duet sung by Little Paul Dombey and his sister Florence. It is a sorrowful song, with Little Paul on his deathbed, being comforted by Florence.

NO. 45

NO. 46

NO. 47

NO. 48

NO. 49

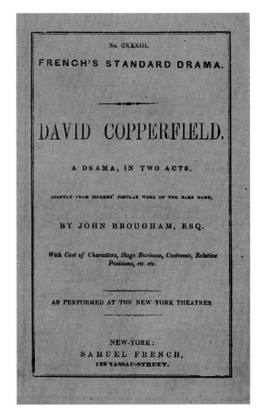

NO. 50

NO. 51

NO. 52

David Copperfield

*D*avid Copperfield *was published in 1850. In the preface, Dickens says: "Of all my books, I like this the best. It will be easily believed that I am a fond parent to every child of my fancy, and that no one can ever love that family as dearly as I love them. But, like many fond parents, I have in my heart of hearts a favorite child. And his name is David Copperfield."*

David Copperfield *is a semi-autobiographical novel. The first eleven monthly parts mirror Dickens's life. Charles Dickens's father, John Dickens (a well-meaning, generous spendthrift), is portrayed as Wilkins Micawber. Faithfully chronicled through David is Charles's own progress from being employed as a boy at six shillings per week in a blacking warehouse, to shorthand reporter, to successful novelist. Of course, "D.C." backwards is "C.D." The best modern dramatic version of* David Copperfield *is the film (released in 1935) starring W. C. Fields, Freddy Bartholomew, Edna Mae Oliver, and Roland Young.*

49. John Dickens. Undated copy of a portrait of Charles Dickens's father, after a painting by John W. Gilbert. The painting by Gilbert was once owned by Henry Fielding Dickens, son of Charles Dickens.

   John Dickens, like Mr. Micawber, lived beyond his income and was once imprisoned in the Marshalsea prison for debt.

50. John Brougham. *David Copperfield. A Drama, in Two Acts.* New-York: Samuel French, no date. French's Standard Drama No. CXXXIII.

   This adaptation was first performed at Brougham's Lyceum, New York City, on January 6, 1851. Brougham was cast as Wilkins Micawber, John Owens as Uriah Heep, and D. S. Palmer as David Copperfield. Mrs. Brougham had the role of Mrs. Peggotty.

51. [Playbill] Weisiger Hall, Louisville, Kentucky. February 18–19, 1869. Announcing performances of scenes from Dickens, including a dramatized sketch, "Peggotty," from *David Copperfield.*

   The Dickens Club in Louisville, Kentucky sponsored this entertainment for the benefit of the Louisville Widows and Orphans Home. Other scenes on the program were from *The Battle of Life* (a rare nineteenth-century performance of this work by Dickens) and *Dombey and Son.*

52. [Sheet Music] George W. Birdseye and M. Keller. *Good night, little blossom.* Boston: Oliver Ditson & Co., 1868.

   This piece foretells in its lyrics the death of David Copperfield's first wife, Dora.

53. [Sheet Music] Charles Jefferys and J. H. Tully. *Dora to Agnes.* New York: Firth, Pond & Co., no date.

   Dora is pictured on her deathbed, asking Agnes Wickfield to marry David Copperfield, and fill her vacant place.

NO. 53

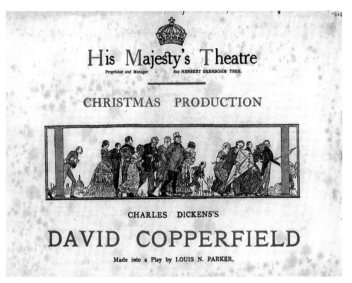

NO. 54

NO. 55

NO. 56

54. [Theater Program] His Majesty's Theatre, London. January 23, 1915. Announcing a performance of *David Copperfield*.

The playwright was Louis N. Parker. Herbert Beerbohm Tree (theater owner and manager) played two roles: Wilkins Micawber and Dan'l Peggotty. David Copperfield was played by Owen Nares, and Little Em'ly by Jessie Winter. This play had uniformly enthusiastic reviews and enjoyed a successful run. The play was revived on February 7, 1921, in Edinburgh by amateur actors for the benefit of the Royal Infirmary.

55. Bransby Williams. Original pencil sketch signed, dated September 10, 1926, depicting Wilkins Micawber.

Bransby Williams starred in Dickensian roles on the stage and in silent films. His sketch appears on the verso of a menu especially prepared for the Gloucester Rotary Club on this date.

56. [Postcard] *Micawber.* London: G. D. & D., no date [circa early 1900s].

Bransby Williams appears in his role as Wilkins Micawber in *David Copperfield*.

57. [Postcard] *Mr. Bransby Williams.* London: Rapid Photo Co., no date [circa 1900]. The photograph was taken by R. Thiele & Co.

Bransby Williams appears in his role as Uriah Heep in *David Copperfield*.

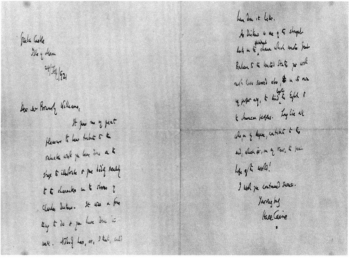

NO. 57   NO. 58

58. Sir Thomas Henry Hall Caine. Autograph letter signed, dated February 24, 1892, to Bransby Williams.

From 1885 to 1913, Caine wrote a number of sensational novels, including *The Shadow of a Crime*, *The Scapegoat*, and *The Prodigal Son*. Caine was a Manxman. Many of his novels are set in the Isle of Man. This two-page letter to Williams is dated Greba Castle / Isle of Man / February 24, 1921, and reads: "It gives me very great pleasure to bear tribute to the valuable work you have done on the stage to illustrate & give bodily reality to the characters in the stories of Charles Dickens. It was a fine thing to do & you have done it well.

Nobody has, or, I trust, could have done it better. As Dickens is one of the strongest links in the spiritual chain which unites Great Britain to the United States your work must have served also, in its own very proper way, to bind together the English & the American peoples. Long live all who, in every degree, contribute to this end, which is, in my view, the great hope of the world! I wish you continued success. Yours very truly Hall Caine."

59. [Poster Playbill] Palace Theatre, Westcliffe-on-Sea. January 20, 1930. Announcing a performance of *David Copperfield.*

The poster depicts Wilkins Micawber. This dramatization was produced by Will King for the Dickens Fellowship. Founded in London in 1902, the Fellowship now has branches worldwide, encourages scholarly interest in Charles Dickens, and publishes a magazine, *The Dickensian.*

60. [Movie Poster] *David Copperfield.* Metro-Goldwyn-Mayer, 1935; re-released 1962.

This film had an all-star cast. Wilkins Micawber was played by W. C. Fields. Fields (born William Duckenfield in 1879) began his career in show business as a juggler at age fourteen. He was in vaudeville; appeared in Paris in the Folies-Bergère and then in the Ziegfeld Follies, and also in George White's Scandals. Fields began his film career in 1915.

Freddy Bartholomew was cast, at the age of eleven, in the title role of *David Copperfield.* He had begun his career at three, on the London stage. Lionel Barrymore, of the famous acting family, was cast in the role of Dan'l Peggotty. Roland Young performed as Uriah Heep.

61. [Photo Stills] Three movie stills titled "David Copperfield," from *David Copperfield,* 1935; re-released 1962.

These scenes show W. C. Fields, Freddy Bartholomew, Roland Young, and Edna Mae Oliver, who played Aunt Betsey Trotwood.

62. [Pressbook] *David Copperfield.* Time-Life Television and BBC-TV, no place, no date.

The pressbook for *David Copperfield* is from the "Once Upon a Classic" public television series hosted by Bill Bixby. This version of *David Copperfield* was financed by a grant from McDonald's Corporation. The pressbook includes a photo of David Yelland in the title role.

63. [VCR Tape] *David Copperfield.* Hallmark Entertainment, released by TNT, 2000.

Michael Richards starred as Wilkins Micawber, Hugh Dancy as David Copperfield, and Sally Field as Betsey Trotwood.

Sally Field won two Oscars: for *Norma Rae* in 1979, and for *Places in the Heart* in 1984. More recently, she is known for her role in *Mrs. Doubtfire* with Robin Williams.

✏ Bleak House

Bleak House, *published in 1853, took aim at the vexatious delays and enormous expense of prosecuting cases in the Court of Chancery. The preface describes a case that had begun twenty years before. Thirty to forty counsel had appeared at one time, seventy thousand pounds had been spent, and the case was no nearer to termination than when it had begun. Dickens writes in the preface that this was a friendly suit, and alludes to many more injustices that he could "rain . . . on these pages."* Bleak House *strikes a chord with those who resent the inequities and inefficiencies of judicial systems.*

Bleak House *tells the story of its sympathetic heroine, Esther Summerson: plain, scarred by smallpox, and born out of wedlock, but kind and compassionate. Her mother, the aristocratic Lady Dedlock, and her father, Captain Horden, pay the wages of sin: they die penniless, and are buried in the potter's field. The villain, Mr. Tulkinghorn, blackmailer of Lady Dedlock, is murdered by his French maid Hortense (whom Dickens modeled after the famous murderess Mrs. Manning). Justice is partially served in* Bleak House: *evil is punished, but an inheritance is frittered away.*

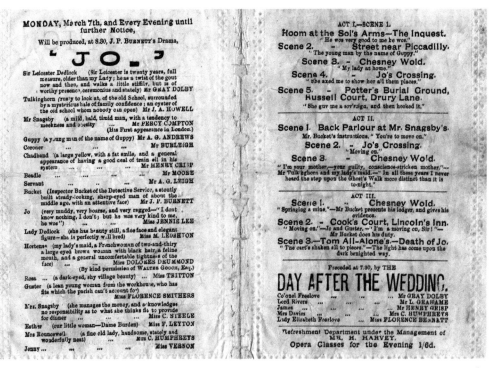

NO. 64

64. [Theater Program] Theatre Royal Olympic, London. March 7, 1881. Announcing a performance of *Jo*, written and produced by J. P. Burnett.

The serial publication of *Bleak House* was completed in September, 1853. From that time until 1870, about nine versions appeared on stage. However, upon Dickens's death in 1870, a host of stage versions were produced. This playbill is for the performance at the Theatre Royal Olympic, London on March 7, 1881 "and Every Evening until further Notice." Jennie Lee starred as Jo. The *Athenaeum* for February 26, 1876 says: "Miss Jennie Lee, a young lady known principally in burlesque, plays the part of 'Jo' with a realism and a pathos difficult to surpass . . . ."

In Dickens's novel, as Jo lies dying, he recites the Lord's Prayer. The Examiner of Plays prohibited the performance of Jo's recitation of the Lord's Prayer. This censorship reflected the British government's attempt to secularize theatrical performances.

65. George Lander. *Bleak House; or, Poor "Jo." A Drama in Four Acts*. London: John Dicks Press, Ltd., no date. Dicks' Standard Plays No. 388.

This play was first staged at the Pavilion Theatre, London on March 27, 1876. In this version, Jo's script (not following the instructions by the Examiner of Plays) includes a partial recitation of the Lord's Prayer in the final scene.

NO. 65

66. [Newspaper Clipping] "Miss Jennie Lee as Jo." *Illustrated Sporting and Dramatic News*, February 26, 1876.

Miss Jennie Lee is shown as Jo in *The New Dramatic Version of Bleak House*. Jennie Lee was to make the role of Jo her own. She acted the role many times, the last time when in her seventies at the Lyric Theatre, London on February 7, 1921, as a benefit for the Charles Dickens Children's Library.

67. [Sheet Music] Fitz James O'Brien and Thomas Baker. *Bleak House Ballads No. 1 Beginning the World*. New York: Horace Waters, 1863.

The cover has a quotation from Bleak House: "And with a parting sob he began the world / Not this world—Oh not this! The world that sets / this right."

NO. 66

68. [Pressbook] *Hard Times*. Granada Television and WNET/13, New York, 1977.

Hard Times is the least dramatized of any of Dickens's novels, having appeared fewer than three dozen times in a dramatic form between 1854, when the book was published, and 1985. This teleplay aired in the United Kingdom on Grenada TV and in the United States on the PBS station WNET. *Hard Times* portrays the harsh impact of the Industrial Revolution on the working poor, and is Dickens's most important book in the social-reform arena.

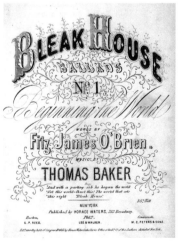

NO. 67

❧ A Tale of Two Cities

The historical novel A Tale of Two Cities *was completed by Dickens in 1859. Dickens's friend Thomas Carlyle, author of* The History of the French Revolution, *provided background information for the book. The action of the story takes place during the French Revolution, and revolves around three principal characters: Sydney Carton, a dissolute, drunken barrister having good intentions but incapable of achieving them; Charles Darnay, a French aristocrat of the St. Evremond family, charged with treason by the revolutionaries; and attractive Lucie Manette. Both Carton and Darnay are in love with Lucie, who loves Darnay. At the climax, Carton sacrifices himself and goes to the guillotine in Darnay's place, so that Darnay may be restored to Lucie.*

A Tale of Two Cities *was one of Dickens's favorites. He said that he would have liked to have had the role of Sydney Carton in a dramatization of the novel.* A Tale of Two Cities *endures as a classic lover's triangle. The dissolute Carton acts nobly in the end.*

69. Thomas Carlyle. Undated reproduction of a line drawing by Samuel Lawrence, engraved by J. C. Armytage.

   WITH: Thomas Carlyle. Autograph letter initialed, undated, and addressed on verso to Leigh Hunt.

   The friendship between the reclusive Scottish Puritan Thomas Carlyle and the outgoing, convivial Dickens seems unlikely. Carlyle, a writer of serious non-fiction, once referred to *Pickwick Papers* as "trash." However, Dickens and Carlyle shared an interest in social reform; their mutual concern helped to cement their friendship. Carlyle's later anti-democratic opinions, especially his conclusion that the ideal leader is the "Strong Just Man," a forerunner of Fascist ideology, did not coincide with Dickens's views. Nevertheless, their friendship endured despite this clash of ideas.

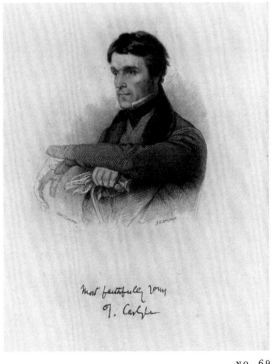

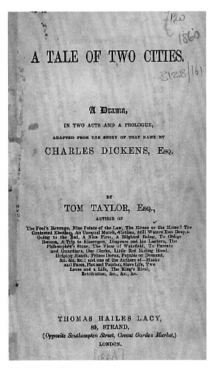

NO. 69   NO. 70

70. Tom Taylor. *A Tale of Two Cities. A Drama.* London: Thomas Hailes Lacy, no date.

This play, the first dramatization of *A Tale of Two Cities*, was first performed at the Lyceum Theatre, London on Monday, January 30, 1860. The play states that Charles Dickens "in the kindest manner superintended the production of the Piece." Mr. Villiers played Sydney Carton, Mr. Forrester played Charles Darnay, and Kate Saville played Lucie Manette. Madame Celeste, who managed the Lyceum Theatre had two roles: in the first act, as Colette Dubois; and in the first and second acts, as the villainous Madame Defarge. Most critics praised the play as being faithful to the novel, and declared it a success. However, others wrote that the play was too long and would probably be abridged.

71. Lieutenant Colonel the Reverend Freeman Wills and the Reverend Canon Langbridge. *The Only Way. A Dramatic Version in a Prologue and Four Acts of Charles Dickens' A Tale of Two Cities.* London: Frederick Muller Ltd., 1942.

The frontispiece is a photograph of Sir John Martin-Harvey as Sydney Carton.

72. [Movie Poster] *A Tale of Two Cities.* Metro-Goldwyn-Mayer, 1935; re-released 1962.

This film starred Ronald Coleman as Sydney Carton. The screenwriters were W. P. Lipscomb and S. N. Behrman. The film was produced by David O. Selznick and directed by Jack Conway.

Coleman, who acted in both silent and sound films, was nominated for academy awards as best actor for *Bulldog Drummond* and *Condemned* (both 1929) and won an academy award for *A Double Life* in 1948. In the 1935 production of *A Tale of Two Cities*, Donald Woods was cast in the role of Charles Darnay; Basil Rathbone was St. Evremonde, and Edna Mae Oliver was cast as Miss Pross. Edna Mae Oliver had the role of Aunt Betsey Trotwood in the 1935 MGM production of *David Copperfield*.

A Tale of Two Cities, with Ronald Coleman, had excellent reviews and was re-released in 1951 and 1962.

73. [Photo Stills] Three untitled stills showing scenes from *A Tale of Two Cities*, 1935.

The first still shows Ronald Coleman and Elizabeth Allen, who played Lucie Manette. The second includes Ronald Coleman, Elizabeth Allen, and Edna Mae Oliver as Miss Pross. The third shows Sydney Carton, the little seamstress, and various aristocrats on their way to the guillotine.

☙ Great Expectations

fter appearing serially in All the Year Round, Great Expectations *was published in three volumes in 1861. While now considered to be one of Dickens's most important works, the novel was staged infrequently in the nineteenth century.*

Great Expectations *tells the story of Pip's love for Estella, a frivolous young woman who lives with her wealthy foster aunt, Miss Havisham. Miss Havisham had been left at the altar by an early lover; in revenge, she adopts Estella and raises her to hate all men. Pip, the recipient of large sums of mysterious origin, assumes an extravagant lifestyle and is led to believe that Miss Havisham is his benefactor. In fact, Pip is the heir of the escaped convict Abel Magwitch. As a boy, Pip had befriended Magwitch, who was subsequently deported to Australia, where he made his fortune. Magwitch risks all to return and make himself known to Pip as his benefactor. Magwitch is apprehended, sentenced to death, and dies in prison. Pip is reduced to poverty, as is Estella, now a widow. Pip and Estella marry at last, their "great expectations" gone, and live a simple life together. Youthful humiliation, lover's follies, and the sinister effects of prosperity and rank—all make* Great Expectations *a serious and still relevant story.*

74. [Pressbook] *Great Expectations.* Universal Pictures, 1934.

This film was directed by Stuart Walker and produced by Stanley Bergerman. The cast included Henry Hull as Magwitch, Francis L. Sullivan as Jaggers, Jane Wyatt as Estella, and Florence Reed as Miss Havisham.

Francis L. Sullivan had other Dickensian roles: as Mr. Crisparkle in *Edwin Drood* (1935), and as Mr. Bumble in *Oliver Twist* (1948).

75. [Movie Poster] *Great Expectations.* Universal Pictures Corporation, 1947.

The script for this film was by David Lean, Ronald Neame, and Anthony Havelock-Allan. The film was directed by David Lean, and produced by Ronald Neame. The film is generally considered to be one of the best ever made based on a Dickens novel. It starred John Mills as Pip, Francis L. Sullivan as Jaggers, Alec Guinness as Herbert Pocket, and Jean Simmons as Estella.

Sir Alec Guinness later received an academy award for best actor for his role in *The Bridge on the River Kwai* (1957). He played other Dickensian roles: as Fagin in *Oliver Twist* (1948), as Marley's Ghost in *Scrooge* (1970), and as William Dorrit in *Little Dorrit* (1987).

ON CHRISTMAS EVE young Pip, a boy of ten, is visiting the graves of his father, mother and brothers, when Magwitch, a convict, suddenly appears from behind a tombstone and commands the frightened child to fetch him food, clothing and a file, the last-named to free himself from the heavy irons on his legs. In helping the man Pip wins his eternal gratitude. Magwitch has escaped from prison for the sole purpose of killing Compeyson, the man who stole his wife from him, but in a very short while he is recaptured.

A year later Pip is sent for by Miss Havisham, an eccentric and morbid middle-aged woman who continually broods over the distant past when the man of her heart deserted her at the altar. Her vengeance on Fate for this disappointment has led her to adopt a beautiful girl named Estella for the sole purpose of bringing her up to hate men and to make life as miserable as possible for the opposite sex. With Pip as a prospective victim life takes on a glow of sinister anticipation. When the boy

•

Authentic Dickens Atmosphere in "Great Expectations"

"GREAT EXPECTATIONS" comes to the screen with the real Dickens flavour untouched, right out of the pages of one of the most human, absorbing and dramatic novels conceived by this greatest of English novelists, an ever-living classic of literature for all time. The story of "Great Expectations" will never grow old. It is just as fascinating and thrilling to-day as it was when Dickens wrote it, almost a hundred years ago, in his beloved house at Gadshill. The story is full of descriptions of the countryside surrounding his home, of the Kentish lanes he loved so well; but it is also vivid with scenes of the London of his day, for Dickens was a great cosmopolitan figure and could write of that great city and its people with more understanding than any writer has been able to do.

One of the most interesting scenes in "Great Expectations," is the Cheapside Inn, "Lily and the Swan." The various signs on it, such as "Coffee Room," "Coach Office," etc., were faithfully copied from books such as Cruikshanks' "Days of Dickens" and actual places in which Charles Dickens himself stayed.

The inn itself is of the hotel variety and is not to be confused with the ordinary public house. The "Coffee Room" in such inns was always the rendezvous of the better class, while the lower class took their drinks in the "tap room." Quite often, the post office was part of the inn, as was also the booking office for coaches in those days.

So much attention was paid to getting the proper Dickensian flavour by Universal in the making of this film, that hardly a detail was overlooked. For example "Jaggers" home, where a great deal of the action in the story takes place, is dignified in the extreme, the furniture suiting perfectly its decidedly massive master. The selection of Chippendale and Hepplewhite furniture, the pieces of old needlework on the walls and chairs, and the fine sporting prints, the dumb waiter table, silver, etc., all go to make up a most interesting and realistic picture.

NO. 74

[45

76. [Photo Stills] Three stills titled "Great Expectations," from *Great Expectations*, 1947.

These stills show: Estella and Pip; young Pip and the convict Magwitch; and (many years later) adult Pip and his secret benefactor, the elderly Magwitch.

77. [Movie Poster] *How Bella Was Won.* Thomas Edison Films, 1911 (undated reproduction).

Dickens's *Our Mutual Friend* has rarely been dramatized. However, Thomas Edison Films in 1911 produced three films based on the novel: *Eugene Wrayburn*; *How Bella Was Won*; and *Bella Wilfer's Return*.

78. [Photo Stills] Two untitled stills showing scenes from *Our Mutual Friend,* no date.

Masterpiece Theater (PBS) produced a seven-part dramatization of *Our Mutual Friend*, made possible by a grant from Mobil Oil Corporation. This series had a distinguished cast, including Jane Seymour as Bella Wilfer, Leo McKern as Mr. Boffin, and Alfie Bass as Silas Wegg.

Jane Seymour starred in a number of film and TV mini-series. She also had her own dramatic series, *Dr. Quinn, Medicine Woman*. Leo McKern had important roles in a number of films, but is probably best remembered as Rumpole of *The Bailey*. Alfie Bass played Mr. Goldberg in the British comedy series *Are You Being Served?*

The first movie still shows actors and actresses from the Masterpiece Theater production of *Our Mutual Friend*: Leo McKern as Mr. Boffin, Jane Seymour as Bella Wilfer, and Alfie Bass as Silas Wegg. The second still is a photo of Polly James as Jenny Wren. Wren is the disabled girl who earns her living making doll clothes in *Our Mutual Friend*.

79. Charles Dickens. *The Mystery of Edwin Drood*.
London: Chapman and Hall, 1870.

Despite failing health, Dickens decided to write a mystery story. This decision was probably influenced by the popularity of mystery novels written by his friend, Wilkie Collins: notably, *The Moonstone* and *The Woman in White*. It is ironic that *The Mystery of Edwin Drood*, unfinished because of Dickens's death, should have engendered more controversy than any of his more important works. The identity of the murderer of Edwin Drood was unknown to the publishers, Chapman and Hall, who in a page appended to the last number, stated: "All that was left in manuscript of *Edwin Drood* is contained in the Number now published—the sixth. . . . The only notes in reference to the story that have since been found concern that portion of it exclusively, which is treated in the earlier Numbers. Beyond the clues therein afforded to its conduct or catastrophe, nothing whatever remains . . . ." However, John Forster, close friend and confidant of Dickens, said that John Jasper was the murderer. Furthermore, Charles Dickens, Jr. said that his father had told him that Jasper would be disclosed as the killer. Charles Collins (brother of Wilkie Collins), husband of Dickens's daughter Kate, and the designer of the parts cover, also weighed in. He said that Dickens had insisted that Jasper, shown in the upper right hand corner of the cover looking thoughtfully at Edwin and Rosa, wear a long scarf with which he would strangle Edwin. Nevertheless, over the years, and despite this

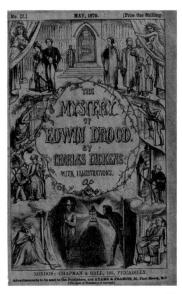

NO. 79

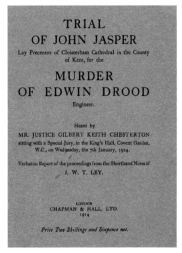

NO. 80

contemporary evidence, scores of books have been published offering solutions to the mystery and conclusions to the novel. These include *The Mystery of Edwin Drood Complete*, in which the novel was purportedly finished by Dickens, from the afterworld, through a spiritualist medium. The "medium" went on to state that the next book to be published by Dickens from the spirit world would be *The Life and Adventures of Bookley Wickleheap*. Thankfully, this was never published. Even R. Austin Freeman, creator of the *Dr. Thorndyke Mysteries*, had a hand at *Edwin Drood*, writing a spoof, *The Mystery of Angelina Frood*.

80. G. K. Chesterton, et al. *Trial of John Jasper*. London: Chapman & Hall, Ltd., 1914.

Because of the difficulty in staging an unfinished novel, there have been few dramatizations of *Edwin Drood*. However, two notable trials of John Jasper for the murder of Edwin Drood were performed in 1914. Exhibited here is the *Trial of John Jasper . . . for the Murder of Edwin Drood* under the auspices of the Dickens Fellowship, London Branch.

The "trial" was held on January 7, 1914, at King's Hall, Covent Garden. The judge was G. K. Chesterton. Other notables in the cast were Bransby Williams, Arthur Waugh, and J. K. Prothero. George Bernard Shaw was foreman of the jury. Other members of the jury included writers W. W. Jacobs, Hilaire Belloc, Max Pemberton, and Arthur Morrison.

The trial had a farcical conclusion. Jasper was found guilty of manslaughter, and neither the prosecutor nor the judge would accept the verdict. The judge's final verdict was: "My decision is that everybody here, except myself, be committed for Contempt of Court. Off you all go to prison without any trial whatever!"

81. John M. Patterson, editor. *Trial of John Jasper for the Murder of Edwin Drood*. Philadelphia: Philadelphia Branch Dickens Fellowship, 1914.

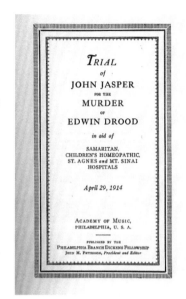

NO. 81

The second Drood "trial" exhibited here was held on April 29, 1914, at the Academy of Music, Philadelphia. It was a benefit in aid of the Samaritan, Children's Homeopathic, St. Agnes, and Mt. Sinai Hospitals. It was arranged by Judge John M. Patterson, who was president of the Philadelphia branch of the Dickens Fellowship. The trial court consisted of the judge, Pennsylvania Supreme Court Justice John P. Elkin; and prosecutors John C. Bell, Attorney General of Pennsylvania, and John M. Patterson, Judge of Common Pleas. Defense counsel was John R. K. Scott, Congressman at Large from Pennsylvania. Curiously enough, this trial resulted in the acquittal of John Jasper for lack of evidence.

82. [Advertisement] *The Mystery of Edwin Drood*. Universal Pictures, 1934.

A Universal pressbook advertising *The Mystery of Edwin Drood* on the inside rear cover. Dramatizations of Dickens's unfinished novel have been few and far between. In 1935, this first talking picture of *Drood* was released by Universal. It had a distinguished cast, including Claude Rains (as John Jasper), who later was nominated for academy awards in *Mr. Smith Goes to Washington* (1939), *Casablanca* (1943), *Mr. Skeffington* (1944), and *Notorious* (1946). Heather Angel, who had roles in *Barclay Square* (1933) and *The Informer* (1935), was cast as Rosa Bud. Francis L. Sullivan (cast as Mr. Crisparkle) had played Jaggers in the 1934 production of *Great Expectations*.

83. [Cassette Tape] *The Mystery of Edwin Drood, the Solve-It-Yourself Musical*. New York: PolyGram Records, 1986.

In 1986 Broadway took an unusual approach to dramatizing *Edwin Drood*. At each performance the audience voted on the solution to the mystery and picked the murderer. On opening night in 1986 the audience came up with the highly unlikely solution that Edwin was not murdered at all!

A Christmas Carol

Since the late 1800s, thousands of versions of the Carol *have appeared on stage, film, and television. The redemption and spiritual rebirth of the miser Scrooge, and Scrooge's kindness to Tiny Tim and the Cratchits, all send a message that has become so identified with the spirit of Christmas that* A Christmas Carol *is probably Dickens's most lasting legacy.*

84. [Movie Poster] *A Christmas Carol.* Metro-Goldwyn-Mayer, 1938.

Charles Dickens's *A Christmas Carol* has inspired more dramatizations than any of his books except *Oliver Twist*. In the twentieth century alone, hundreds of "Carols" were performed not only on film and TV, but in stage musicals and in school auditoriums.

This version was written by Hugo Butler, produced by Joe Mankiewicz, and directed by Edwin L. Marin. Reginald Owen played Scrooge; Gene Lockhart was Bob Cratchit; and Terry Kilburn played Tiny Tim. Reginald Owen had a variety of film and stage roles over a period of forty years, including a part in *A Tale of Two Cities* in 1935. Gene Lockhart and his wife Kathleen Lockhart both appear in this film. Their daughter June Lockhart is probably best remembered for her role as Ruth Martin in the TV series *Lassie*.

85. [Movie Poster] *A Christmas Carol.* Renown Pictures and United Artists, 1951.

The screenplay was written by Noel Langley, and the film was produced and directed by Brian Desmond Hurst. The film starred Alastair Sim as Scrooge. Sim played a variety of roles on stage and in film productions, ranging from comedies to "whodunits." Also in the cast was Kathleen Harrison, who had played in *Oliver Twist* (1948) and in *Pickwick Papers* (1952).

86. [Movie Poster] *Scrooge.* National General Pictures, 1970.

Leslie Bricusse wrote the screenplay, the music, and the lyrics, and was the executive producer. The film was directed by Ronald Neame. It starred Albert Finney as Scrooge, Alec Guinness as Marley's Ghost, and Dame Edith Evans as the Ghost of Christmas Past.

Albert Finney was a distinguished actor, having been nominated for academy awards for his performances in *Tom Jones*, *Murder on the Orient Express*, *The Dresser*, and *Under the Volcano*. Alec Guinness played in a number of Dickens dramatizations, including *Oliver Twist* and *Great Expectations*. Dame Edith Evans played in a dramatization of *David Copperfield*.

87. [Photo Stills] "Albert Finney in 'Scrooge.'"

WITH: Untitled still showing Edith Evans as the Ghost of Christmas Past from *Scrooge*, 1970.

88. [Theater Poster] *A Christmas Carol.* The Cleveland Playhouse, 1980.

This poster advertises the Doris Baizley dramatization of *A Christmas Carol*, the Cleveland Playhouse production directed by Will Rhys and performed for the 1980–81 Christmas season.

89. [Drawing] Charles Berliner. *A Christmas Carol, The Cleveland Playhouse, Cleveland, Ohio. Marley's Ghost and Scrooge,* 1981.

An original hand-colored sketch, drawn and signed by Charles Berliner. Berliner, a native of San Francisco, designed the scenery and costumes for Doris Baizley's production of *A Christmas Carol,* originally produced at the Mark Taper Forum in Los Angeles and directed by John Dennis. Baizley's *Carol* was performed annually from 1977 to 1981.

Charles Berliner has designed scenery and costumes for plays, musicals, films, and TV. He is one of the few theatrical designers to receive a design-artist fellowship from the National Endowment for the Arts.

90. [Photographs] Charles Berliner. Photo of an original sketch titled "Mark Taper Forum / Los Angeles CA. 1977."

WITH: Untitled photo of Wayne S. Turney, circa 1977.

The Doris Baizley production of *A Christmas Carol* is unique. It is performed as a play within a play, in which a poverty-stricken theater company attempts to present *A Christmas Carol.* All of the participants play dual roles. The stage manager doubles as Scrooge, the director as Marley, and the prop-boy as Tiny Tim. This commedia dell'arte approach is enhanced by Charles Berliner's costumes and set designs. Exhibited here is a photograph of Berliner's original sketch of a wardrobe trunk (twelve feet high, and eight feet wide) which opens up and from which the actors emerge. The trunk is also designed so that Scrooge's bed emerges from it, and so that it can act as a platform for street scenes. The photograph of actor Wayne S. Turney shows him opening the trunk with a huge key.

NO. 88   NO. 89

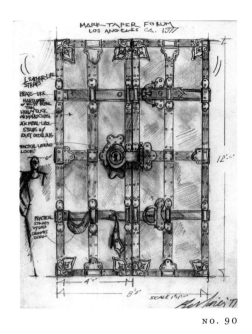

NO. 90   NO. 91

91. [Photographs] Charles Berliner. Photo of an original sketch titled "Center Theatre Group / of Los Angeles / Mark Taper Forum."

WITH: Untitled photo of Alfre Woodard as the Ghost of Christmas Past, circa 1977.

A photograph of Charles Berliner's original sketch of the costume for the Ghost of Christmas Past, together with a photograph of Alfre Woodard, who was cast in the role in the Doris Baizley production of *A Christmas Carol*. Woodard also played Mrs. Cratchit. In the cast of the TV series *Desperate Housewives*, Alfre Woodard plays Betty Applewhite.

92. [Pressbook] *A Christmas Carol*. Entertainment Partners, Inc. and IBM, 1984.

This version of *A Christmas Carol* was presented by IBM on CBS TV, December 17, 1984, and starred George C. Scott as Scrooge.

Scott, having denounced the Hollywood academy awards as a "meaningless self-serving meat parade," won the best-actor award for *Patton* in 1970. He refused to accept the Oscar. Scott played other Dickensian roles on television, including Fagin in *Oliver Twist*.

93. [Photo Still] Untitled still showing Mickey Mouse as Bob Cratchit, from *Mickey's Christmas Carol*, 1984.

Mickey Mouse had been featured in more than a hundred cartoons between 1928 and 1953. He was then absent from the screen because of the popularity of other Walt Disney characters, principally Donald Duck. His return in *Mickey's Christmas Carol* was his first animated show in thirty years, and was aired on NBC TV. Other Disney characters were in the cast, including Minnie Mouse, Pluto, Donald Duck, and of course, Uncle Scrooge McDuck.

94. [VCR Tape] *A Christmas Carol*. Hallmark Entertainment, released by TNT, 1999.

Patrick Stewart, who played Scrooge, is probably best known for his role in *Star Trek, the Next Generation* and its sequels, and for his Shakespearean performances on stage.

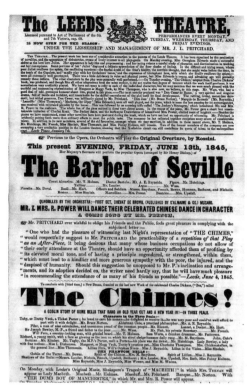

NO. 95

NO. 96

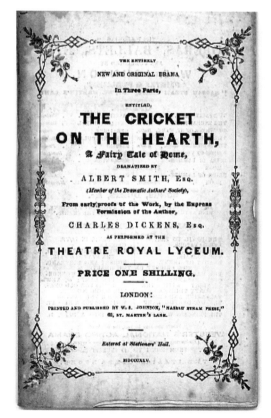

THE ENTIRELY
NEW AND ORIGINAL DRAMA

In Three Parts,

ENTITLED,

THE CRICKET
ON THE HEARTH,

A Fairy Tale of Home,

DRAMATIZED BY

ALBERT SMITH, Esq.

(Member of the Dramatic Authors' Society),

From early proofs of the Work, by the Express
Permission of the Author,

CHARLES DICKENS, Esq.

AS PERFORMED AT THE

THEATRE ROYAL LYCEUM.

PRICE ONE SHILLING.

LONDON:

PRINTED AND PUBLISHED BY W. S. JOHNSON, "NASSAU STEAM PRESS,"
60, ST. MARTIN'S LANE.

Entered at Stationers' Hall.

MDCCCXLV.

NO. 97

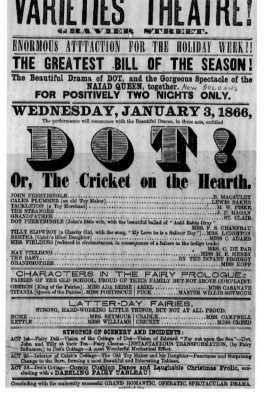

NO. 99

The Chimes, The Cricket on the Hearth, and The Battle of Life

Three of Dickens's Christmas books, in addition to A Christmas Carol, *have had frequent dramatizations. They echo similar themes: rich vs. poor; redemption; and spiritual rebirth.*

95. [Playbill] The Leeds Theatre, Leeds. June 13, 1845. Announcing a performance of *The Chimes!*

    The theater manager, Mr. Pritchard, printed on June 4, 1845, a playgoer's testimony suggesting in part that attendees "should have an opportunity afforded them of profiting by its [i.e. *The Chimes'*] elevated moral tone, and of having a principle engendered, or strengthened, within them, which must lead to a kindlier and more generous sympathy with the poor, the injured, and the despised of humanity." Frances Ternan, the mother of Ellen Ternan (who was later to become Dickens's mistress) is listed as having the part of Lady Macbeth in an upcoming performance of Shakespeare's play. Miss Fanny Ternan, a sister of Ellen, is also listed for her upcoming part in an unattributed play, *The Admiral's Pet.*

96. [Sheet Music] M. Jullien. *The Chimes: Jullien's Chimes Quadrilles.* London: no place, no date. (Publisher's name and date trimmed from bottom of front cover).

    The illustrations on the cover of this piece of sheet music are similar to illustrations in the first edition in book form of *The Chimes*, showing Trotty Veck leading Mrs. Chickenstalker to the dance.

97. Albert Smith. *The Cricket on the Hearth, A Fairy Tale of Home.* London: W. S. Johnson, 1845.

    The Cricket on the Hearth was published in 1846. However, before publication Dickens joined forces with the playwright Albert Smith and the famous acting pair Mr. and Mrs. Keeley of the Lyceum Theater to produce a stage version from early proof sheets of the book. The result was *The Cricket on the Hearth, A Fairy Tale of Home.* The cast included Mr. Keeley as Caleb Plummer, and Mrs. Keeley as Dot. The play was a huge success. Smith's original version at the Lyceum had more than sixty performances.

98. [Playbill] Boston Academy of Music. December 27, 1860. Announcing a performance of *Dot!*

    One of the most famous dramatizations of *The Cricket on the Hearth* appeared in 1859, as *Dot!* The famous playwright Dion Boucicault wrote the script, and also produced *Dot!* in America. It was first staged in 1859 at New York's Winter Garden. It then went on tour in America and Great Britain. Boucicault's *Dot!* combined Shakespearean characters with characters from Dickens's *Cricket.* Shakespeare's Oberon, Titania, and Puck appear in the cast.

99. [Playbill] Varieties Theatre, New Orleans. January 3, 1866. Announcing a performance of *Dot! Or, The Cricket on the Hearth.*

    Lewis Baker, who was cast as Caleb Plummer, had starred as Micawber in an early dramatization of *David Copperfield* at Barnum's Museum in Philadelphia. He then took the show on the road and played in New Orleans and San Francisco. The famous actress Henrietta Baker Chanfrau was cast as Dot Peerybingle in *Dot!* She was perhaps best known for her role as Portia in the famous performance of *Julius Caesar* on November 25, 1864, in which the three Booth brothers (Junius, Edwin, and Lincoln assassin John Wilkes) were cast as Cassius, Brutus, and Mark Antony. The 1866 performance advertised by this playbill was staged in the Confederate State of Louisiana only a few months after General Robert E. Lee had surrendered the Army of Northern Virginia to end the War between the States.

100. [Sheet Music] T. L. Rowbotham. *The Criket* [*sic*] *on the Hearth*. London: M. Tolkien, no date.

This work is dedicated to Charles Dickens and has "Cricket" misspelled. Each quadrille is dedicated to a character or characters in the Christmas story: Dot and Baby, John Peerybingle, Tilly Slowboy, etc.

101. Carl Goldmark and A. M. Willner. *Das Heimchen am Herd*. Leipzig: Emil Berte & Cie., 1896.

In 1896 Carl Goldmark composed music for a stage version of *The Cricket on the Hearth*: an opera, *Das Heimchen am Herd*, which was first performed in Leipzig and later in Vienna. The libretto was by A. M. Willner. This copy of the libretto has text in both German and English.

102. [Playbill] Theatre Royal, Lyceum [London]. January 4–5, 1847. Announcing a performance of *The Battle of Life*.

The Battle of Life was published in 1846. As in the case of *The Cricket on the Hearth*, Dickens arranged with Albert Smith to write a play based on the Christmas story, and with the Keeleys to stage the production at the Lyceum. Dickens himself took a hand in the play,

NO. 100   NO. 101

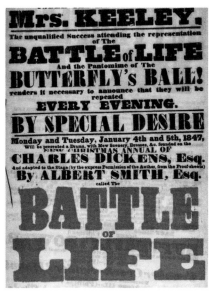

attended rehearsals, made suggestions, and generally supervised its production. This play-bill states that the play is "adapted to the Stage (by the express Permission of the Author, from the Proof-sheets) by Albert Smith, Esq." Mr. and Mrs. Keeley were both in the cast. However, as a play *The Battle of Life* was a failure. It was staged fewer than thirty times between 1847 and 1900.

103. "Morna" [pen name of Captain Thomas O'Keefe]. *The Battle of London Life; or, Boz and his Secretary.* London: George Peirce, 1849.

This early spoof of Dickens's *Battle of Life* recounts a series of bawdy adventures of "Boz" and a male secretary, Mr. Phillipson. The two are portrayed traveling about London, with Dickens ("Boz"), in search of unusual characters who might populate his novels. At the end of these sketches Mr. Phillipson is exposed as a plant, being a member of the London Private Detective Police.

This book is one of the most imaginative publications taking advantage of Dickens's fame. *Charles Dickens by Pen and Pencil* (a website exhibition completed in 2006 for the Charles Dickens Museum, London) describes Thomas O'Keefe as ". . . an Irish gentleman and a sort of 'man about town.'" The illustrations for the book are by George Augustus Sala.

104. John Braham. Undated engraving after H. Adlard.

Braham, shown here as he appeared in 1800, was man-ager of the new St. James's Theatre. In 1836, Braham accepted *The Village Coquettes*, a comic opera written by Charles Dickens, with music by John Hullah.

105. Charles Dickens. *The Village Coquettes: A Comic Opera.* London: Richard Bentley, 1836.

The Village Coquettes was dedicated to the comedian J. P. Harley, who, together with John Braham, was in the cast.

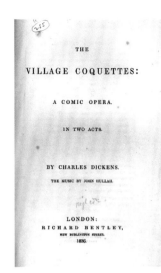

NO. 105

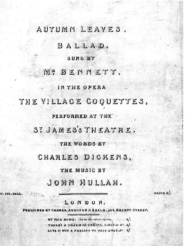

NO. 106

NO. 107

The play was first produced at the St. James's Theatre on December 26 (Boxing Night), 1836.

106. [Sheet Music] Charles Dickens and John Hullah. *Autumn Leaves*. London: Cramer, Addison & Beale. No date [circa 1836 or 1837].

"Autumn Leaves" is from *The Village Coquettes: A Comic Opera*.

107. [Sheet Music] "Boz" (Charles Dickens) and Henry Russell. *The Ivy Green*. New York: Wm. A. Pond & Co., 1838. "25th Edition" on the cover.

"The Ivy Green" is from *The Village Coquettes: A Comic Opera*, by Charles Dickens, and published by Richard Bentley in 1836.

108. J. P. Harley. Undated reproduction of a portrait.

The comedian is pictured here in the leading role from *The Strange Gentleman*, a play by Dickens, published in 1837. "The Great Winglebury Duel" in *Sketches by Boz* was the basis of this farce. The first performance of *The Strange Gentleman* was given on September 29, 1836. Harley played the title role for sixty nights. Another in the cast was Madame Sala, mother of George Augustus Sala.

109. [Playbill] Theatre Royal, Liverpool. September 5, 1838. Announcing the performances of *Wild Oats, The Strange Gentleman*, and *Loan of a Lover*.

Harley acts here in the lead role as "The Strange Gentleman."

NO. 108

NO. 109

56]

110. J. P. Harley. Autograph letter signed, January 15, 1857, to "My Dear Sir" [H. Watkins, Esq.].

A jocular letter to a friend, albeit on mourning stationery, with reference to a well-known English comic song, "The Old English Gentleman."

111. "Boz" [Charles Dickens]. *The Strange Gentleman; A Comic Burletta, in Two Acts.* London: Chapman and Hall, 1837 [reprint, published in 1871].

Only a few copies now survive of the first edition of *The Strange Gentleman*, produced in 1837. The copy exhibited here is a facsimile reprint.

112. Charles Dickens. *Is She His Wife? Or, Something Singular. A Comic Burletta in One Act.* Boston: James R. Osgood and Company, 1877.

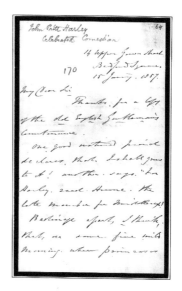

NO. 110

In 1837 Dickens wrote this play for J. P. Harley, who had starred in *The Strange Gentleman* and in *The Village Coquettes*. The rights were purchased by John Braham for one hundred pounds and the play was produced at the St. James's Theatre on March 6, 1837. However, *Is She His Wife?* had little success and enjoyed only a short run.

The play was published in America by James R. Osgood in 1877. The 1837 cast included Harley as Felix Tapkins and Madame Sala as Mrs. Peter Limbury. The cast also included Mr. Gardner as Peter Limbury. Gardner would later have roles in dramatizations of *Oliver Twist* and *Nicholas Nickleby*.

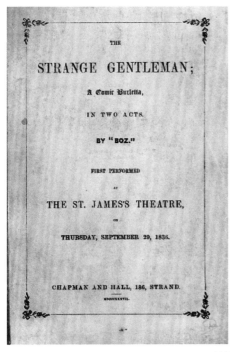

NO. 111

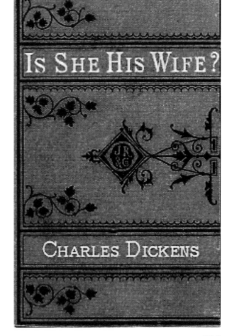

NO. 112

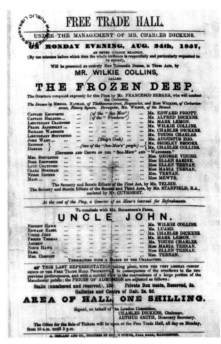

113. [Playbill] Tavistock House Theatre [London]. January 8, 1857. Announcing a performance of *The Frozen Deep*.

> *The Frozen Deep* has important roles in the life of Charles Dickens. It represents in part
> the inspiration for *A Tale of Two Cities*, one of Dickens's most successfully dramatized nov-
> els. Unfortunately it was also a catalyst for Dickens's marital difficulties and the eventual
> breakup of his marriage to Catherine.
>
> In 1856 Dickens urged his friend Wilkie Collins to write a play based on the life and
> tragic death of Sir John Franklin and his companions. Franklin was a distinguished naval
> hero, having fought at Copenhagen and with Nelson at Trafalgar. In 1845 Franklin set sail
> with two ships and a crew of 129 officers and men in an effort to find the Northwest
> Passage. The company were lost and never heard from again. The expedition apparently
> became icebound and perished from fatigue, hunger and the extreme cold. Dickens wrote a
> prologue for Collins's play *The Frozen Deep* and collaborated to such an extent with Collins
> that it might be said that the finished play was a joint effort of the two writers and friends.
> In the performance advertised by this playbill, Richard Wardour (played by Dickens) and
> Frank Aldersley (played by Collins) vie for the love of Clara Burnham, played by Dickens's
> daughter Mary. The play reaches its climax when Richard Wardour saves his rival Aldersley
> from death and restores him to Clara. Wardour dies as a result of his efforts to save
> Aldersley. This plot foreshadows the plot of *A Tale of Two Cities* when Sydney Carton goes
> to the guillotine in place of Charles Darnay, who is restored to Lucie Manette.
>
> *The Frozen Deep* was performed at the Tavistock House Theatre on January 6, 8, 12,
> and 14, 1857; this playbill is for the second performance. Charles Dickens, Jr., Alfred
> Dickens, Kate Dickens, and Dickens's sister-in-law, Georgina Hogarth, are also in the cast.

114. [Playbill] Free Trade Hall, Manchester. August 24, 1857 [reproduction made in 2005].
Reproduction of the original playbill announcing a performance of *The Frozen Deep*.

58]

After which, the Historical Drama, in Two Acts, by J. R. PLANCHE, Esq., called

CHARLES XII.

CHARLES THE TWELFTH, (King of Sweden)	Mr. FRANK STONE, A.R.A.
GENERAL DUCKERT, (Governor of Stralsund)	Mr. COE,
COLONEL REICHEL,	Mr. PETER CUNNINGHAM,
GUSTAVUS DE MERVELT,	Mr. JOHN TENNIEL,
MAJOR VANBERG, (under the assumed name of FIRMANS)	Mr. AUGUSTUS EGG, A.R.A.
ADAM BROCK, (a Wealthy Farmer)	Mr. F. W. TOPHAM.
TRIPTOLEMUS MUDDLEWORTH, (Burgomaster)	Mr. WILKIE COLLINS.
ULRICA, (Daughter of Vanberg)	Miss FANNY YOUNG.
EUDIGA, (Daughter of Adam Brock)	Mrs. HENRY COMPTON.

SCENERY.

Public Ground and Inn.	Mr. TELBIN.
A Room in a Village Inn,	Mr. PITT.
Parlour at Adam Brock's,	Mr. PITT.
The Ramparts of Stralsund,	Mr. THOMAS GRIEVE.
Old Tapestry Chamber,	Mr. LOUIS HAGHE.
Another Chamber,	Mr. PITT.
Hall of Audience,	Mr. PITT.

To conclude with, (twenty-third time) an original Farce, in One Act, by Mr. CHARLES DICKENS and Mr. MARK LEMON, entitled

MR. NIGHTINGALE'S DIARY.

Mr. NIGHTINGALE,	Mr. FRANK STONE, A.R.A.
Mr. GABBLEWIG, (of the Middle Temple)	
CHARLEY BIT, (a Boots)	
Mr. POULTER, (a Pedestrian and Cold-Water Drinker)	Mr. CHARLES DICKENS.
CAPTAIN FLOWER, (an Invalid)	
A RESPECTABLE FEMALE	
A DEAF SEXTON,	
TIP, (Mr. Gabblewig's Tiger)	Mr. AUGUSTUS EGG, A.R.A.
CHRISTOPHER, (a Charity Boy)	
SLAP, (professionally Mr. Flormiville—a Country Actor)	Mr. MARK LEMON.
Mr. TICKLE, (Inventor of the celebrated Compounds)	
A VIRTUOUS YOUNG PERSON IN THE CONFIDENCE OF "MARIA"	Mr. WILKIE COLLINS.
LITHERS, (Landlord of the "Water Lily")	Miss FANNY YOUNG.
ROSINA,	Mrs. COE.
SUSAN,	

The Proscenium by Mr. CRACE. The Theatre constructed by Mr. SLOMAN, Machinist of the Royal Lyceum Theatre. The Properties and Appointments by Mr. G. FOSTER. The Costumes by Messrs. NATHAN, of Titchborne Street. Perruquier, Mr. WILSON. Prompter, Mr. COE.

☞ THE WHOLE PRODUCED UNDER THE DIRECTION OF MR. CHARLES DICKENS.

The Local Arrangements under the superintendence of Mr. William Sudlow.

Doors open at Six o'Clock. To commence at exactly Seven o'clock; when the whole of the audience are particularly recommended to be seated. Tickets to be had at the Offices of the Philharmonic Society, Exchange Court. Stalls in the Body of the Hall and Boxes, 7s. 6d.; Gallery Stalls, 5s. 6d.; Gallery Seats, 3s. 6d.

ENTRANCE TO ALL PARTS OF THE HALL FROM HOPE STREET.

A. IRELAND AND CO., PRINTERS, PALL MALL, MARKET STREET, MANCHESTER.

NO. 115   NO. 116

By courtesy of the Manchester City Council, Department of Libraries and Theaters.

Dickens took his amateur Company of Strolling Players on the road, and arranged to stage performances of *The Frozen Deep* in Manchester in August 1857. Up to this time, the cast of *The Frozen Deep* had consisted of Dickens's friends and members of his family. However, Dickens decided that professional actresses should now take the female parts. Three of these roles were then filled by members of an acting family, the Ternans: mother Frances, and two daughters, Maria and Ellen. This playbill (exhibited through the courtesy of the Manchester Library and Information Service: Manchester Arts Library) is a copy of one for the performance at the Free Trade Hall, Manchester on August 24, 1857 and lists Wilkie Collins, Charles Dickens, and the Ternans in the cast. Dickens and Ellen Ternan performing together in *The Frozen Deep* marked the beginning of a relationship that would develop into a notorious liaison. When they first met in 1857, she was eighteen, and he was forty-five.

115. Ellen Ternan. Undated reproduction of a photograph taken circa 1857.

By courtesy of the Dickens House Museum, London.

116. [Playbill] Philharmonic Hall, Liverpool. September 3, 1852. Announcing a performance of *Mr. Nightingale's Diary*.

In 1851 Charles Dickens collaborated with Mark Lemon to write a one-act farce entitled *Mr. Nightingale's Diary*. Dickens and his amateur Company of Strolling Players went on tour with the play for the benefit of the Guild of Literature and Art. The Guild provided assistance to authors and artists, supplementing the pensions then provided them by the government and by certain theaters in which they had performed. Dickens had six roles in the farce. Others in the cast were Mark Lemon and Wilkie Collins. *Mr. Nightingale's Diary* shared the bill with *Used Up*, in which Dickens also performed as an actor.

[59

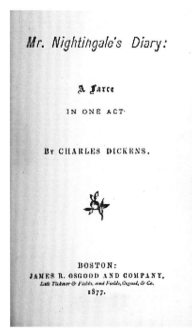

NO. 117

NO. 119

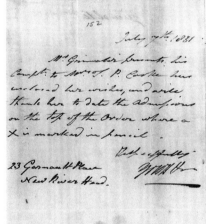

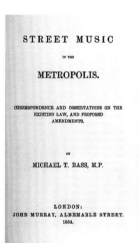

NO. 120

NO. 120

NO. 121

NO. 122

NO. 123

NO. 124

60]

117. Charles Dickens. *Mr. Nightingale's Diary: A Farce in One Act*. Boston: James R. Osgood and Company, 1877.

Mr. Nightingale's Diary was published in 1877 as first performed at Devonshire House, London in 1851. The cast consisted of Dudley Costello as Mr. Nightingale, Charles Dickens as Gabblewig, Mark Lemon as Slap, and Wilkie Collins as Lithers.

118. Charles Dickens and Wilkie Collins. *No Thoroughfare. A Drama, in Five Acts and a Prologue*. New York: Robert M. De Witt, no date [circa 1868]. De Witt's Acting Plays, Number 14.

119. Charles Fechter. Reproduction of a portrait drawn on stone by Richard Lanel, published August 10, 1864, by J. Mitchell, Bookseller and Publisher to the Queen, and by Special Appointment to the Emperor Napoleon III.

No Thoroughfare, a collaboration of Charles Dickens and Wilkie Collins, was first staged on December 26, 1867, at the New Adelphi Theatre, London. At that time, Dickens's most recent novels, *Great Expectations* in 1861, and *Our Mutual Friend* in 1865, had appeared difficult to adapt to the stage, and relatively few productions had resulted from them. *No Thoroughfare* was written specifically for the stage and was successful, enjoying a run of two hundred performances at the Adelphi. Its success was due in large measure to the acting of Charles Fechter as Obenreizer. Fechter is said also to have directed the play. Fechter was a noted French actor who starred in Shakespearean tragedies as well as in productions such as *Ruy Blas* and *Lady of Lyon*. *No Thoroughfare* achieved great popularity in England, France, and the United States; Dickens felt that the play would not have achieved this popularity had it not been for Fechter's guidance. In appreciation, Dickens contributed an enthusiastic article entitled "On Mr. Fechter's Acting" to the August 1869 number of *The Atlantic Monthly*. The article served to introduce Fechter to the American public.

120. Joseph Grimaldi. Undated reproduction of a drawn portrait.

WITH: Joseph Grimaldi. Autograph letter signed, July 7, 1831, to Mrs. T. P. Castle.

Grimaldi was the subject of Charles Dickens's book *Memoirs of Joseph Grimaldi*, edited by "Boz," and published by Richard Bentley in 1838. A famous clown for whom circus clowns are still nicknamed "Joeys," Grimaldi left an outline of his memoirs, which eventually came into the possession of the publisher Bentley, who gave the manuscript to Dickens for completion and editing. Thus, Dickens edited and wrote portions of the book, although the exact extent of his involvement is unknown.

In the letter, Grimaldi gives instructions apparently clarifying an order for merchandise.

121. Michael T. Bass, M.P. *Street Music in the Metropolis*. London: John Murray, 1864.

One type of show biz that Charles Dickens did not participate in, promote, or enjoy was metropolitan "street music." In the 1860s organ grinders, generally accompanied by a trained monkey, would station themselves outside a residence in an upscale neighborhood of London and play their organs until the resident opened the door and paid the monkey a shilling. Then the organ grinder with his monkey would go away and repeat the performance a few doors down the block. This blackmail finally prompted Michael T. Bass,

M.P. to introduce a bill in Parliament to stop this street music. Bass solicited letters from influential Londoners to join his crusade. Charles Dickens wrote a letter of support, which was also signed by a number of writers and artists, including Alfred Tennyson, John Everett Millais, Wilkie Collins, and Thomas Carlyle. Dickens's letter reads in part "Your correspondents are . . . driven nearly mad, by street musicians. . . . houses are beleaguered by discordant hosts seeking to be bought off." Another proponent of Bass's bill was Charles Babbage, the brilliant mathematician and an originator of the modern computer. Babbage submitted statistics to support his argument. In his letter to Bass, he states that over a ninety-day period, he was harassed 165 times by street music: nine times by brass bands, ninety-six times by organ grinders, and sixty times by organ grinders with monkeys. Bass published his argument, with supporting letters, in *Street Music in the Metropolis*. The volume is a rare item of Dickensiana.

122. [Sheet Music] J. M. Field and James G. Maeder. *The wery last observations of Weller, Senior, to Boz, on his departure from London.* Boston: W. H. Oakes, 1842.

WITH: Dr. Oliver Wendell Holmes. *The Stars Their Early Vigils Keep.*
Boston: W. H. Oakes, 1842.

Charles Dickens visited America for the first time in 1842. As a famous author, he was wined and dined by celebrities wherever he went. When he visited Boston he was given a dinner by local dignitaries on February 1. This event included the two songs printed in these publications. The first piece was written and sung by J. M. Field. The lyrics consist of seven verses. Verses five and six comment on the copyright laws and how they have been violated in America by piracies of Dickens's novels. The second song was written by Dr. Oliver Wendell Holmes, who sang it at the same dinner on February 1. Holmes was a Boston Brahmin and considered Boston to be "The intellectual hub of the Universe." Holmes, in addition to being a prominent writer of poems and essays (his most famous poem is "Old Ironsides"), was dean of the Harvard Medical School and author of several important medical works. Coincidentally Holmes, in common with Dickens, was a social reformer and held Unitarian beliefs.

Dickens, during his visit to America, ventured as far west as St. Louis. There, Dickens wished to be taken further west. The group traveled on for a few more miles, and had dinner on the prairie. One of the dishes served was buffalo tongues (repellent to conservationists and vegetarians today). Dickens was impressed by the seemingly endless horizon, which contrasted so starkly with Britain's landscape.

123. Leigh Hunt. Undated reproduction of a drawn portrait, showing Hunt at the age of sixty-six.

WITH: Autograph letter signed, November 5, 1838, to R. H. Horne. Mounted with a franked envelope addressed in Hunt's hand to Horne.

Hunt, a friend of Dickens, was an essayist, publisher of literary journals, and poet. He had a tempestuous career, once being jailed for two years for libel against the Prince Regent. Despite his success as a writer, he was improvident and constantly in financial difficulties. The letter is addressed to fellow writer R. H. Horne and "all who may be in his confidence on the subject." Hunt was apparently writing after an illness, as he expresses gratitude for the friendship of all those who "have enabled the wounded old bird to sing again."

124. [Playbill] Miss Kelly's Theatre, Soho. September 20, 1845. Announcing an amateur performance of Ben Jonson's *Every Man in His Humour.*

WITH: A reproduction of a portrait of Charles Dickens in the role of Captain Bobadil.

This play was staged for the benefit of Leigh Hunt. Dickens had the starring role; others in the cast were Douglas Jerrold and Mark Lemon.

125. [Announcement Card] General Theatrical Fund. London, 1846.

On April 6, 1846, Charles Dickens was chairman of the First Anniversary Festival of the General Theatrical Fund, held at the London Tavern. The General Theatrical Fund was established in 1839 to help aged or invalid actors not eligible for aid under either the Drury Lane or the Covent Garden Fund. Note that tickets cost one guinea each, a stiff price in 1846. This fundraising event was planned to attract a wealthy celebrity audience. As chairman, Dickens made a speech in which he commented: "When old actors passed for the last time from behind that glittering row of lights, they did not pass away into gloom and darkness, but retired into the cheerfulness and light of a contented home."

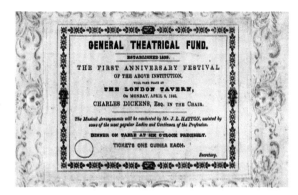

NO. 125

126. [Playbill] Theatre Royal, Haymarket. March 13, 1848. Announcing a performance of *The Merry Wives of Windsor.*

In 1848 Dickens decided to produce an amateur performance to aid the endowment of a perpetual curatorship of Shakespeare's house. He assembled a group of amateur actors, including Mark Lemon, George Cruikshank, and John Forster. Shakespeare's *The Merry Wives of Windsor* was selected and Dickens produced and directed the production, and acted in it. Rotund Mark Lemon was in the cast as Falstaff, and Dickens as Shallow. On the same evening, Elizabeth Inchbald's farce *Animal Magnetism* was performed with Dickens and Lemon in the cast.

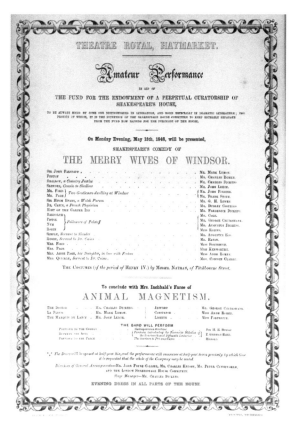

NO. 126

[63

127. [Playbill] Devonshire House [London]. May 16, 1851. Announcing a performance of *Not So Bad As We Seem: or, Many Sides To a Character.*

This performance of Bulwer Lytton's new comedy was presented for Queen Victoria and Prince Albert under the auspices of the Guild of Literature and Art. Charles Dickens had the role of Lord Wilmot. John Forster, Douglas Jerrold and Wilkie Collins were also in the cast.

128. [Playbill] Theatre Royal, Tavistock House [London]. January 8, 1855. Announcing a performance of James R. Planché's *Fortunio and His Seven Gifted Servants.*

Charles Dickens loved Christmas, and celebrated the season in several ways: through his numerous Christmas stories of course, but also through personal and family endeavors. It would seem that Dickens viewed Christmas not so much as a religious holiday, but as a season of good food and drink, and a time for the gathering of family and friends for entertainment and hijinks. Dickens loved children, and during each Christmas season, he held children's parties at which he performed conjuring tricks, sang comic songs, and presided at a festive dinner followed by dancing. He also produced Twelfth Night plays, the cast consisting of the children, adult friends, and members of his family. A typical Twelfth Night performance is announced on the playbill exhibited here. For this performance, on January 8, 1855, the nursery at Tavistock House was converted to a theater with a stage. Planché's farce *Fortunio and His Seven Gifted Servants* was produced. The cast included Wilkie Collins as Wilkini Collini, Mark Lemon as Strongback, and Dickens in two roles: as Mr. Passe, and as Mr. Measley Servile. Among the children, Mr. Ainger is Alfred Ainger, a little friend of the Dickens children. Henry Dickens is Mr. H, and Edward Dickens, not yet three, plays Mr. Plornishmaroontigoonter.

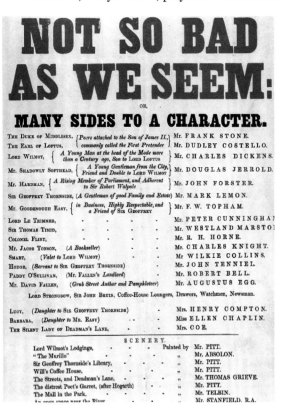

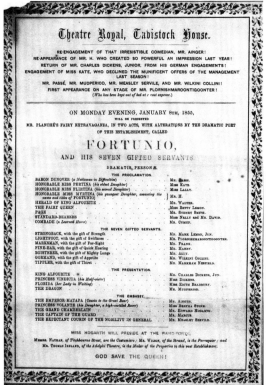

NO. 127   NO. 128

129. [Playbill] Tavistock House [London]. June 19, 1855. Announcing performances of *The Lighthouse* and *Mr. Nightingale's Diary*.

In 1855 Charles Dickens's friend Wilkie Collins wrote a two-act melodrama entitled *The Lighthouse*. Dickens liked the play and suggested that they stage it, with a cast of amateur actors, in the children's theater at Dickens's home, Tavistock House. The theater seated only twenty-eight, so the play was performed on June 15, 16, 18 and 19. Dickens composed "The Song of the Wreck," which was sung by his daughter Mamie Dickens. The scenery was painted by Clarkson Stanfield, R.A., who illustrated many of Dickens's books. Dickens, who often used the stage name "Mr. Crummles," had the lead role of Aaron Gurnoch. Wilkie Collins played Martin Gurnoch. Others in the cast were Mark Lemon, and Dickens's sister-in-law Georgina Hogarth. *Mr. Nightingale's Diary* was performed after intermission.

130. Charles Dickens. *A Christmas Carol. As Condensed by Himself, for His Readings*. Boston: Lee and Shepard, 1892. One of a series of ten dramatic readings, entitled *Charles Dickens's Dramatic Readings as Read in America*.

During the twentieth century, *A Christmas Carol* was often dramatized; however, before 1900 the *Carol* had been staged rarely, by comparison to other works by Dickens. H. Philip Bolton, author of *Dickens Dramatized*, states that one reason *A Christmas Carol* was less popular on stage during the nineteenth century was due to a "Victorian diffidence about staging sacred matters." In fact, the Examiner of Plays censored quotations of Scripture and unflattering depictions of ecclesiastical figures (cf. items 64 and 65).

Nevertheless, when Dickens in 1853 decided to embark on a career of giving public

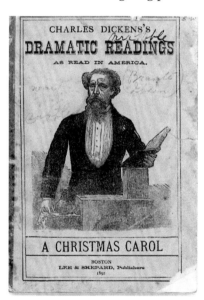

NO. 129 NO. 130

readings, the first reading he selected was from *A Christmas Carol*, and it was given at Birmingham Town Hall on December 27, 1853. This and two subsequent readings at Birmingham attracted a total of six thousand people. Dickens's new career was launched with great success and monetary gain.

Dickens then gave public readings throughout Britain, and in 1868 he made a reading tour in America. He performed for the most part in Boston and New York, but he also appeared throughout New England and as far south as Baltimore. Dickens visited President Johnson, but when Dickens was to give a reading in Boston on February 24, Johnson was impeached. Dickens was dismayed when the public furor over the impeachment resulted in empty seats for the first time during the reading tour. On the back cover of this book is an advertisement for "The Grand Dickens Cosmorama" by George B. Bartlett (a cosmorama was a series of stage processions and tableaux vivants).

131. Charles Dickens. *The Story of Little Dombey*. London: Bradbury & Evans, 1858.

WITH: *A Christmas Carol*. London: Chapman & Hall, no date.

WITH: *David Copperfield*. Boston: Ticknor and Fields, 1868.

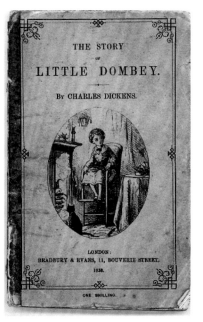

Dickens's reading tour in America in 1868 was a huge financial success. Total receipts were $228,000 and Dickens earned a profit, after all expenses had been paid, of twenty thousand pounds. (One pound was approximately equivalent to five U.S. dollars of that period.)

However, Dickens's health had begun to fail. Despite the fact that he was in almost constant discomfort or pain, upon his return to England he contracted to give one hundred additional readings throughout Great Britain for eight thousand pounds. These began in the fall of 1868 and continued until his final readings in 1870.

In 1858 Dickens authorized the publication of reading editions. These were condensations originally made by Dickens for use as texts at his readings. Exhibited here are three examples of these editions.

NO. 131

132. [Announcement Card and Ticket Stub] Rotunda, Dublin, 1869.

The card announces Dickens's final readings in Dublin on January 11, 12, and 13, 1869. On the eleventh he performed *A Christmas Carol* and the *Trial From Pickwick*; on the twelfth, *David Copperfield* and *Bob Sawyer's Party* from *Pickwick*; and on the thirteenth, *Sikes and Nancy* from *Oliver Twist*, *Mrs. Gamp* from *Martin Chuzzlewit*, and *Boots at the Holly Tree Inn*. The ticket stub is from the performance on the thirteenth.

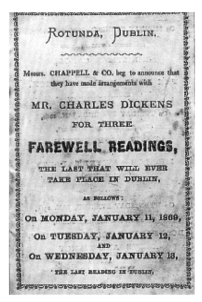

NO. 132

66]

133. [Ticket Stub] St. James's Hall [London]. January 25, 1870.

This ticket stub is from one of Dickens's final readings, given at St. James's Hall, London on January 25, 1870. A highlight of this reading was *Sikes and Nancy*, from *Oliver Twist*. Dickens became so personally involved in repeatedly acting out the murder scene where Sikes bludgeons Nancy that he sometimes had to be helped from the stage, and often collapsed in his dressing room.

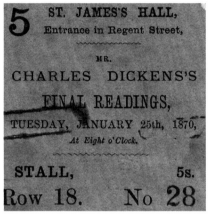

NO. 133

NO. 134

134. Charles Dickens. *Sikes and Nancy*. London: Henry Sotheran & Co., 1921.

This edition is a reprint of a copy of the privately printed edition formerly in the collection of Sir Henry Irving. Irving's copy, containing the penciled-in stage directions, agrees with the made-up copy used by Dickens himself. Pages 38 and 39 contain the murder scene in which Bill Sikes bludgeons Nancy to death. Dickens gave his final reading on March 15, 1870, at St. James's Hall, London. Weakened by a series of strokes and suffering from emotion and fatigue, Dickens addressed his audience for the last time: "From these garish lights I vanish now for evermore with a heartfelt, grateful, respectful and affectionate farewell."

135. [Photograph] Maguire's Opera House. No place, no date. Reproduction of an original photograph, exhibited through the courtesy of the California Historical Society, FN-16862.

Thousands of miles away from Charles Dickens's London, and a continent away from Boston, was the cultural center of the West Coast—San Francisco, with Tom Maguire and his opera house. Maguire was illiterate and a gambler, but also a shrewd impresario and promoter. He billed top attractions into his opera house and later into Baldwin's Theater, where he served as manager.

NO. 135

136. [Playbill] Maguire's Opera House, San Francisco. July 17, 1861. Announcing a performance of *Nicholas Nickleby.*

This playbill announces the ninth night of the engagement of Joseph Jefferson as Newman Noggs in Dickens's novel *Nicholas Nickleby.* Joseph Jefferson was a celebrated comedian who had many Dickensian roles: in *Nicholas Nickleby, Oliver Twist, The Cricket on the Hearth,* and *Dombey and Son.* He was most famous for his role as Rip Van Winkle (in a stage version of Washington Irving's short story).

137. [Playbill] Baldwin's Theater, San Francisco. No date. Announcing a performance of *Little Nell and The Marchioness!*

A 1951 facsimile (issued to members of The Book Club of California) of the original playbill for the week of August 24, 1879, advertising Baldwin's Theater, which was managed by Tom Maguire. The playbill announces the appearance of Lotta Crabtree in *Little Nell and The Marchioness!* from Dickens's *The Old Curiosity Shop.* The playwright was John Brougham.
   Lotta Crabtree was a child prodigy. She had sung and danced in mining camps in the 1850s and was a friend of the Spanish dancer and actress Lola Montez. In the performance advertised on this playbill, Lotta Crabtree not only acts, but plays banjo solos and does "her famous clog dance." Lotta gave "Lotta's Fountain" to San Francisco in 1875.

138. [Playbill] Maguire's Opera House, San Francisco. August 27, [no year]. Announcing a performance of *Mazeppa.*

A 1951 facsimile (issued to members of The Book Club of California) of the original August 27, 1863 playbill.

WITH: Reproduction of an original photograph of Adah Isaacs Menken, exhibited through courtesy of the California Historical Society, FN-19627.

Adah Isaacs Menken was born near New Orleans in (or around) 1835. Facts concerning her family name and early life are obscure. She was left in poverty at an early age, and appeared on the stage in New Orleans and other American cities. In 1856 she married Alexander Isaacs Menken, and thereafter bore his name through various matrimonial ventures, including marriage to heavyweight fighter "Benicia Boy." During her stage tour in San Francisco, Menken got to know many local writers, including Bret Harte, Mark Twain, and Joaquin Miller. In 1864 she performed in London's Astley's Theatre as Mazeppa. In this role Menken appeared almost nude, strapped to a running horse. In England and France she became intimate with many literary men: Algernon Charles Swinburne, Charles Reade, and Charles Dickens, to whom she dedicated a volume of verse, *Infelicia.* Adah Isaacs Menken played Dickensian roles, including Pip in *Great Expectations. Nicholas Nickleby* was performed for her benefit in New York City in 1862.

139. Adah Isaacs Menken. *Infelicia.* London, Paris, and New York: 1868.

This copy belonged first to the author Bayard Taylor, who has signed twice on preliminary leaves (once with the date August, 1868); a later owner was the author and bibliophile A. Edward Newton. The book is dedicated to Charles Dickens and includes a reduced facsimile letter in which Dickens accepts the dedication.

MAGUIRE'S OPERA HOUSE

Proprietor .... Thomas Maguire
Treasurer .... W. Stevenson

Ninth Night of the Engagement of

MR. JEFFERSON,

The Celebrated American Comedian

Wednesday Evening, July 17, 1861

The Performance will commence with the celebrated Drama adapted from Charles Dickens' Novel of

Nicholas Nickleby

Newman Noggs, - Mr. Jefferson
Nicholas Nickleby .... Mr. H. A. Perry
Ralph .... Mr. Waldron
Squeers .... Mr. Leman
John Browdie .... Mr. J. B. Booth
Smike .... Mrs. Sophie Edwin
Tompkins .... Mr. Franks
John .... Mr. Mack
Kate Nickleby .... Miss Jennie Mandeville
Mrs. Squeers .... Mrs. Woodward
Miss Squeers .... Mrs. Saunders
Miss Price .... Mrs. H. A. Perry

To conclude with the Celebrated Farce of the

SPECTRE BRIDEGROOM

Diggory, - - Mr. Jefferson
Nicodemus .... Mr. Waldron
Aldwinkle .... Mr. Leman
Vauntington .... Mr. Genevieve
Paul .... Mr. Franks
Georgia .... Mr. Mack
Georgina .... Miss Jennie Mandeville
Lavina .... Mrs. Perry

NOTICE—During Mr. JEFFERSON'S Engagement, seats may be secured three days in advance.

CALHOUN Printer, No. 535 Washington Street, S. F.

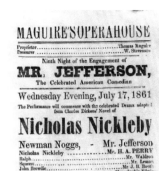

Programme Extra.

THIRD WEEK and MOST BRILLIANT SUCCESS OF

LOTTA!

Supported by Mr. ED. MARBLE and the Great Baldwin Co.

EVERY EVENING DURING THE WEEK,

Will be presented the beautiful creation of Charles Dickens' genius, framed and set to the Drama by John Broughton, entitled,

LITTLE NELL and THE MARCHIONESS!

LITTLE NELL .... LOTTA
THE MARCHIONESS
OLD GRANDFATHER TRENT .... Mr. A. D. BRADLEY
DICK SWIVELLER .... Mr. C. B. BISHOP
DANIEL QUILP .... Mr. J. W. JENNINGS
SAMPSON BRASS .... Mr. JAS. BARROWS
NED TRENT .... Mr. F. H. THOMPSON
MR. SLUM .... Mr. JAS. A. HERNE
CODEY JACK .... Mr. J. W. WILKES
BROKEN BADGER .... Mr. PAUL LOGAN
FOXEY JOE .... Mr. DAVID BELASCO
ABDULLAH .... Master HERMAN JAHN
BIGGINS .... Mr. L. PAUL
BIGGINS .... Mr. B. DAVID
MORTON .... Mr. SIMPSON
SHORMAN .... Miss OLIVE WEST
MRS. QUILP .... Miss JEAN CLARA WALTERS
MRS. JARLEY .... Miss MOLLIE REVEL
SALLY BRASS .... Miss NELLIE WETHERALL
MISS JINIWIN .... Miss RUTH COWLES
MRS. SIMMONS .... Miss LAURA COWLES
MRS. GEORGE

The GRAND ORCHESTRA under direction of Mr. H. J. WIDMER will play "The Turkish Review" at each performance.

During the play MISS LOTTA will introduce, for the first time this season, her renowned
BANJO SOLOS,
also, during the Fair Scene, her famous
CLOG DANCE,
and in the Last Act
MEDLEY OF POPULAR AIRS, assisted by Mr. BISHOP.

PROGRAMME OF MUSIC.
By The Baldwin Grand Orchestra, under the direction of
Mr. H. J. WIDMER.

Overture .... Suppe
Mocker Grace Quadrille .... Faust
Song and Chorus—"Little Sweetheart, Come and Kiss Me," for Cornet and Union .... performed by Messrs. Sax Cornet and Mendelyea.
Turkish Review .... Michaelis
Solo—"Solitude Lays" .... Schumann

The FURNITURE used in the setting of this Piece is from the warerooms of F. S. Chadbourne & Co., 735 Market Street.

Lotta Matinee,
SATURDAY, August 30th,
Little Nell and The Marchioness!

SATURDAY NIGHT, August 30th,
FOR THIS NIGHT ONLY,
L'ASSOMMOIR!

SUNDAY NIGHT, August 31st,
LOTTA!
LITTLE NELL and THE MARCHIONESS!

FOR REFRESHMENTS BETWEEN ACTS,
——GO TO——
KITTELBERGER & DOLD'S,
cor. Market and Powell, (under Baldwin's Hotel.)

MAGUIRE'S OPERA HOUSE

T. MAGUIRE .... Proprietor
W. STEVENSON .... Treasurer | C. L. GRAVES .... Stage Manager
S. TUTHILL .... Machinist

THE GREATEST SUCCESS!

—— EVER ACHIEVED IN THIS CITY, IS THIS ENGAGEMENT OF ——

Miss ADAH ISAACS

MENKEN

MAZEPPA!

The Greatest Wonder of the Living Age, whose Personation of Lord Byron's Great Creation,

Is acknowledged by the Thousands who have witnessed it, to be Unparalleled in Daring, and Unapproachably Superior to any other person who has attempted this Perilous Character in the United States.

Miss ADAH Ascends and Descends to and from the Entire Height of this Immense Theater, lashed to the Bare-Back of the Wild Steed, a Feat never accomplished by any other Lady in the World.

—— SHE WILL BE SUPPORTED BY ——
MRS. SOPHIE EDWIN,
FRANK MAYO,
J. B. BOOTH,
And the Full Strength of the Great Star Company.

Thursday Evening, August 27th,

Will be presented the Grand Romantic Equestrian Spectacle of

NO. 136   NO. 137   NO. 138

Gad's Hill Place,
Higham by Rochester, Kent.

Monday June First October 1867

Dear Miss Menken

I shall have great pleasure in accepting your dedication, and I thank you for your portrait as a highly remarkable specimen of photography.

I also thank you for the verses enclosed in your note. Many such enclosures come to me, but few so pathetically written, and fewer still so modestly sent.

Faithfully yours
[Charles Dickens]

NO. 139   NO. 139

140. G. B. Bartlett. *The Carnival of Authors*. New York and London: Samuel French, no date.

Tableau vivant was a form of entertainment that flourished briefly during the nineteenth century, principally in the 1880s. This booklet contains instructions for staging tableaux vivants. The booklet suggests eight elevated platforms (called "booths") for presenting the tableaux: 1. Dickens; 2. Arabian Nights; 3. Tennyson; 4. Scott; 5. Longfellow; 6. Shakespeare; 7. Whittier; and 8. Goethe. The Dickens booth would be used for the following tableaux: on the first night, men and women dressed as Dickens characters would portray scenes from *Nicholas Nickleby*, *Our Mutual Friend*, *A Tale of Two Cities*, *Pickwick Papers*, and *The Old Curiosity Shop*. On the second night excerpts from *Martin Chuzzlewit*, *The Old Curiosity Shop*, *Nicholas Nickleby*, *David Copperfield*, and *Pickwick Papers* would be performed.

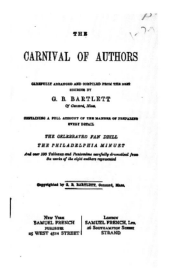

NO. 140

141. [Anonymous] *Authors' Carnival Album*. San Francisco: A. L. Bancroft & Company, 1880.

The *Authors' Carnival Album* records the tableaux vivants staged on September 20, 1880 in San Francisco at the Mechanics' Pavilion. Proceeds from the sale of tickets went to various charitable organizations, including the Ladies Protection and Relief Society, the Young Women's Christian Association, and the Old Ladies Home. The Executive Committee consisted of some of San Francisco's leading citizens, including Charles Crocker and A. S. Hallidie. Dickens tableaux were from *The Old Curiosity Shop*, *David Copperfield*, and *Barnaby Rudge*.

NO. 141

NO. 142

142. [Newspaper] *Frank Leslie's Illustrated Newspaper*. New York, February 28, 1885.

The newspaper contains a full-page sketch of a scene in the Dickens Carnival at Mechanics' Hall, Boston on February 17. The Dickens Carnival was organized by the Women's Educational and Industrial Union of Boston. Over seven thousand tickets were sold. The entertainment consisted of tableaux vivants representing scenes from Dickens's novels, followed by a procession of the characters in costume. The procession pictured here is from *Barnaby Rudge*. It includes Barnaby Rudge with his raven Grip, Gabriel Varden, Dolly Varden, and other characters from the tableau, all parading before a participant posing as Charles Dickens seated at a table.

143. [Photo Still] Untitled still showing Emlyn Williams reading Charles Dickens in 1967.

A publicity photograph and text issued by CBS to publicize Emlyn Williams's one-man show of readings from Charles Dickens. This television performance was aired January 29, 1967. Impersonating Dickens, Emlyn Williams made highly successful tours in Britain and America. Williams appeared in other Dickensian roles, notably as Mr. Dick in the film *David Copperfield* (1970), which starred Dame Edith Evans as Aunt Betsey Trotwood.

144. [Photo Still] Untitled still (1977) showing Roy Dotrice as Charles Dickens.

A photo showing Roy Dotrice as Charles Dickens in the PBS production of *Dickens of London*, which aired in 1977 on Masterpiece Theater.

Dotrice joins Bransby Williams and Emlyn Williams as impersonators of the novelist. Also in the photo are Simon Bell as young Charles Dickens, and Gene Foad as young adult Dickens.

145. [Fair Poster] The Seventh Annual Great Dickens Christmas Fair. Novato, California, no date.

For many years, the San Francisco Bay area has been the locale for an annual Dickens Christmas Fair. The fair has been staged at several different venues around the bay. This poster advertises one of the fairs held in San Francisco in the 1970s. The fair features booths with proprietors dressed in Dickensian costumes. Visitors are encouraged to attend wearing Victorian attire. The Dickens Christmas Fairs are reminiscent of the tableaux vivants of the 1880s.

146. [33 rpm Phonograph Records] *A Christmas Carol and Mr. Pickwick's Christmas*. Decca DLP 8010.

WITH: *An Adaptation of Dickens' Christmas Carol*. Disneyland Records 3811.

WITH: *Lionel Bart's Oliver!* RCA Victor LOCD-2004.

WITH: *Emlyn Williams as Charles Dickens*. Argo Decca Records RG 231.

Many audio recordings derive from Dickens's stories. Exhibited here are four which highlight talented performers portraying Dickens and his work.

First is Charles Laughton telling the story of *Mr. Pickwick's Christmas*, and Ronald Coleman as Scrooge in *A Christmas Carol*. Charles Laughton won an academy award in 1933 for his role in *The Private Life of Henry the VIII*. Other notable performances were as Captain Bligh in *Mutiny on the Bounty* (1935), as Inspector Javert in the movie *Les Misérables* (1935), and as Quasimodo in *The Hunchback of Notre Dame* (1939). Ronald Coleman was always the suave, dignified, romantic hero in both silent and sound films. He starred as Sydney Carton in *A Tale of Two Cities* (1935), and won an Oscar for *A Double Life* in 1948.

Second is a Walt Disney Productions adaptation of *A Christmas Carol* (1974). Mickey Mouse is Bob Cratchit, Donald Duck is Scrooge's nephew, Goofy is Marley's Ghost, and Scrooge McDuck is Scrooge.

Third, in 1962 RCA Victor recorded Lionel Bart's *Oliver!* with its original cast. Clive Revill played Fagin, and Georgia Brown, Nancy. Clive Revill had previously played Sam Weller in *Mr. Pickwick*. Georgia Brown began her career as a cabaret singer, and starred in *The Three Penny Opera*.

Fourth, the great Dickens impersonator Emlyn Williams had a long career as actor, playwright, and director. He wrote and had the leading role in *Night Must Fall* (1935). He had a Dickensian role as Mr. Dick in *David Copperfield* (1970). Williams's readings in the role of Charles Dickens were subsequently released on 33 rpm records.

147. [Newspaper Editorial] "The Old Curiosity Mall." *The New York Times*, April 12, 2005.

This editorial discusses plans for a "Dickens World" in Chatham, England. The article is sarcastically critical of the proposed development, and compares it to Disneyland. It also suggests, tongue in cheek, that perhaps a "Larkin World" at Hull, honoring Philip Larkin, would be appropriate. The English poet and essayist Philip Larkin (who in 1955 was appointed librarian to the University of Hull) prided himself on being out of step with mainstream writers. His first volume of essays, *All What Jazz*, was published in 1970. Among his most famous poems is "Toads." Larkin described himself in the words of a fictitious biographer as "One of those old type natural fouled up guys."

Index

Entries refer to catalogue item numbers, not to pages.

Set in Miller types, designed by Matthew Carter.

Printed in an edition of 1000 copies on Mohawk Superfine paper

by the Studley Press. Designed by Jerry Kelly.